FUNDAMENTALS OF TECHNOLOGY

Volume Three

Second Edition

DeWayne R. Brown, PhD
Derrek B. Dunn, PhD

Ch. 10 Project / Statistic!

XanEdu
Change the course.

D1406536

ISBN: 978-1-58390-230-1 (Vol. 1–3 bundled)
ISBN 978-1-58390-227-1 (Volume 1 only)
ISBN 978-1-58390-228-8 (Volume 2 only)
ISBN 978-1-58390-229-5 (Volume 3 only)

Change the course.

530 Great Road
Acton, Massachusetts 01720
800-562-2147

This book is dedicated to the most influential and inspirational women in Dewayne's life:

Mrs. Dora Mae Hanna Brown Redden (Mother)

Mrs. Josephine Coward Hanna (Grandmother) [deceased]

Dr. Lisa Hope Antoine

Ms. Arneitha Roberta Nesmith

Dr. Cynthia Thompson

CONTENTS

PREFACE

This book is intended to be used for students at vocational, associate or baccalaureate degree programs who are studying to become technicians or technologists. The book will start with a comprehensive review of the past and the present history of technology. The various careers in technology will be covered. The role of the technologist in the technical lab will be emphasized. The book will provide information about student success that will help them with retention and realizing their personal goal. Students will begin preparing for their careers in technology by developing cover letters, writing resumes, learning to critique interviews and will receive valuable advice for effective writing and listening. Topics that will be vital to students' careers, in the private sector and government such as leadership and diversity, will be included. The fundamental mathematics and measurements that are used in various fields in technology is studied. Plotting data and statistics will be covered where MATLAB will be used as the instrumental tool for computation and graphing.

Changes in the Second Edition

- The most extensive improvements in the *Fundamentals of Technology, Second Edition* are:

- Employ and salary information in Chapter 1 has been updated.

- History of Technology has been updated to reflect the second decade of the 21st century.

- The section on Ethics and Professionalism for Computer Professionals in Chapter 2 was updated to reflect new information on copyright laws, trademark, servicemark and patents.

- A new section was added to Chapter 2 to address six types of interviews.

- More information was added in Chapter 2 for preparing for the initial interview (screening interview) and the on-site interview (selection interview).

- A new section was added to Chapter 2 that provide information on the tone of voice during interview.

- A new section was created in Chapter 2 to help students address tough job interview questions.

- There is a new chapter on effective communication skills.

- There is new chapter on leadership and diversity.

- There is a new chapter featuring student success.

To the Student

Today, the key to survival in the fierce job market will involve the embracement of diversity and the employment of people with capable leadership potential. Corporations and their customers have been forced to react not only to the changing face of America, but the mindsets of the global marketplace. Innovation will continue to thrive even in the online world. The demand for professionals to produce, install, and maintain state-of-the-art equipment, train and supervise industry's skilled workers, and support research and development efforts will remain on the rise. This book will allow you to answer questions like:

- How can I start now and continue to persist to my goals of graduation and job employment?

- Am I communicating effectively and managing my time efficiently?

- What challenges am I facing to remain productive in my technical career as corporations reinvent themselves with diversity?

This textbook will provide a lot of information for succeeding in college, preparing for a career after graduation and maintaining your success through your professional years. Emphasis is placed on ethics, attitude, professionalism, communicating effectively, valuableness of find resources and using your time wisely. The authors encourage the students to sharpen their problem-solving abilities by working the math problems because it will help them build their critical thinking skills.

To the Instructor

The text material has been used in the classroom and has worked well for our four-year college students who pursued a bachelor's degree in technology. It usage is encouraged for two-year college students, too. This book is user-friendly for students without a strong background in technology. *Fundamentals of Technology, Second Edition* is recommended to be used as the primary text for Orientation to Technology or Engineering Technology courses or as a supplement for courses requiring the use of applied mathematics, computers, or scientific calculators. The text also may be used in technical or vocational schools.

All chapters of the textbook have a homework section in Appendix A. Chapters 1 – 6 consist of comprehension that will help reinforce the concepts from the chapters. Some of the comprehension will require consulting resources outside the book, such as the internet to stimulate critical thinking. Chapters 7 – 10 contain numerous practical applications, computer simulation/scientific calculator computations, and critical-thinking mathematical problems to help the students to think more abstractly and be able to analyze.

Organization

Chapter 1 will provide an introduction to technology. First the history of technology will be discussed, from the Stone Age through the second decade of the 21th Century. Various growing fields in technology such as Information Technology (IT), Computer Engineering (CET), Biomedical Technology, and Environmental Technology are investigated. The differences among the job responsibilities of scientists, engineers, technologists and technicians are examined.

Chapter 2 focuses on the career development of a technologist. The importance of professionalism and ethics are covered. Emphasis is placed on personal and professional development, work habits and job performance, personal conduct and human relations. Tips and pointers on cover letters, and resumes for hard copy and email are featured. There are samples of cover letters and resumes. Students are taught how to write letters to acknowledge an offer as well as how to reject an offer. The textbook will cover the entire process of preparing for interviews whether if it is an initial or on-site interview and whether it is in person, by telephone, by computer or will be video-conferenced. Addition information on the tone of voice during interviews is provided. There is a valuable section that addresses how to respond to sample tough interview questions.

In **Chapter 3** the job responsibilities of the technologist in the technical laboratory will be discussed. The importance of lab safety training is covered. Some rules for lab safety are offered. How to develop good lab skills is addressed. The types of errors that occur in measurements in the laboratory such as gross, systematic, and random are reviewed. Strategies for reducing these errors are included. Percentage error calculations are done. The importance of significant figures and their effects on computations are emphasized. In addition, how to write lab reports and tips on giving oral reports are discussed in this chapter, too. A brief review of common errors in lab reports is given. Some popular technological tools to enhance performance in the technical laboratory as well as the classroom, such as the scientific graphical calculator and the computer algebraic systems are covered.

Chapter 4 addresses how to communicate effectively. The chapter emphasizes the process of how communication works. Students will learn how to communicate exactly what they want to say and what mode of communication is best for that particular message. In addition, factors that influence your ability to speak clearly and listen critically are discussed. This chapter addresses the four types of communication styles and provides advice on how to communicate if you have that style or dealing with someone else who has that style.

In **Chapter 5** the importance of leadership and diversity are emphasized. Leadership is defined and its attributes and qualities are described. This chapter will help students to develop leadership skills to be successful leaders through education and modeling leadership rubrics. The importance of embracing diversity as a culture is addressed. Factors that affect diversity will be covered to help students appreciate and market the

new direction that corporations are now taking to implement diversity and inclusion in their infrastructures. Students will learn first-hand hoe companies and institutions are re-inventing themselves through diversity matrices and competency models for diversity management from domestic and global perspectives. Students will understand the newly role of Diversity & Inclusion (D&I) practitioners in the corporate and the visionary and strategic planning that they must bring to help corporations remain successful.
.

Chapter 6 explains how student success is beneficial to society. The most potent principles of student success are identified in this chapter. The factors that influence students' success in college are addressed. This chapter is helpful for freshmen students who are making that transition to college by providing advice and recommendations for common changes and common stressors that freshmen can expect in their first year on campus. Student time management is emphasized and some of the common barriers to student time management are discussed. Advice will be offered for improvement of techniques for studying.

Chapter 7 will cover some of the basic mathematics used in the various fields of technology. Topics such as arithmetic, simple algebraic equations, and basic matrix algebra are covered. MATLAB as a software simulation tool for computation will be introduced in this chapter as reinforcement of the learned concepts. Computer software tools such as MATLAB will be valuable for students entering the corporate work environment or graduate school. MATLAB is one of the most powerful and popular software tools for science-related fields on the market. MATLAB is a programming language and data visualization tool. MATLAB has many capabilities for solving problems in engineering, technology, scientific, computing and mathematical disciplines.

Chapter 8 covers measurement systems. First the U.S. customary system of measurement is discussed. Next the metric system is studied. Conversions between the U.S. customary and metric systems are performed. Temperature conversions are done. Mathematical applications that can be solved by the usage of a circle are addressed. The relationship among various units of time is covered. Lastly, students are taught how to effectively determine the time in different time zones.

Chapter 9 emphasizes the fundamentals of graphing data. After data is collected it must be presented to others in a meaningful way. Oscilloscopes, spectrum analyzers, logic analyzers etc. are examples of some of the instruments that display graphical information. Students will learn how to graph linear equations and non-linear equations. Selecting scales for graphs will be reviewed. The concepts of interpolation and extrapolation applications to graphing will be covered. In addition, students will use MATLAB to plot fundamental two-dimensional graphics. They will be able to graph trigonometric functions, such as the sine wave, cosine wave, and the tangent wave. They will be able to graph linear and non-linear equations. Students will be able to label the x- and y-axes. They will be able to give graphs a title name.

Chapter 10 covers the background of statistics. This chapter covers a range of techniques and procedures for analyzing data, interpreting data, and displaying data. In this chapter, students will use MATLAB to perform statistical analyses on data sets. They will compute the mean, standard deviation and variance of data sets by both hand calculation and computer simulation. Students will use MATHLAB to create histograms. They will apply MATLAB curve fitting techniques to data sets for straight-line approximation, quadratic approximation and other higher order approximations.

About the Authors

Dr. Dewayne Randolph Brown is a Full Professor of Computer Systems Technology Department within the School of Technology at North Carolina Agricultural & Technical State University in Greensboro, North Carolina, United States of America. Dr. Brown teaches undergraduate and graduates courses in electronic and wireless communications. In addition, Dr. Brown has taught orientation to technology courses for nine-teen years. Dr. Brown has written four previous textbooks relevant to the field of technology, *Fundamentals of Technology* (XanEdu, 2012), *Fundamental Mathematics for Electronics and Information Technology* (XanEdu, 2008), *Mathematics for Technologists in Electronics, Second Edition* (Prentice-Hall, 2002), and *Mathematics for Technologists in Electronics* (Pearson Custom Publishing, 2000). Dr. Brown received his Bachelors of Science in electrical engineering from the University of South Carolina in 1990. Dr. Brown received his Masters of Science in electrical engineering from North Carolina Agricultural & Technical State University in 1992. Dr. Brown received his Ph.D. in electrical engineering from Virginia Polytechnic Institute and State University in 1997. Dr. Brown has been a member of Association for Technology, Management, and Applied Engineers (ATMAE) formerly known as the National Association of Industrial Technology (NAIT) since 2000. Dr. Brown is a Certified Senior Technology Manager (CSTM) within ATMAE.

Dr. Derrek B. Dunn is currently a Full Professor and Chairperson of the Department of Technology in the School of Business and Technology at University of Maryland at Eastern Shore (UMES). Dr. Dunn has taught college level courses in such fields as Wireless Communication Systems, Computer Networks, Telecommunication Management, Global Positioning Systems, and Optical Systems.

Dr. Dunn received his Bachelor of Science in Electrical Engineering and a Bachelor of Science in Mathematics from North Carolina A&T State University. He also received a Master of Science in Electrical Engineering, Master of Science in Mathematics and a Doctor of Philosophy in Electrical Engineering from Virginia Polytechnic Institute and State University.

Dr. Dunn bring nearly 15 years of experience in teaching and research on learners and learning at a distance, and experience on the use of distance education in technology and engineering.

Dr. Dunn's past experience with The Association of Technology, Management, and Applied Engineering (ATMAE) formerly known as the National Association of Industrial Technology (NAIT) includes membership of NAIT/ATMAE for the past eleven years, certified industrial technologist, ATMAE accreditation training, Regional Director - Student Division and member and elected to a second term as Vice-President of the Electrical, Electronics and Computer Technology (EECT) Division and is currently the President of the Electrical, Electronics and Computer Technology (EECT) Division.

CHAPTER 7
Mathematics

CHAPTER 7
MATHEMATICS

7.1 INTRODUCTION

The decimal number system is the common number system used in the United States for all computations. The decimal number system will pave the way for us to understand others number systems such as the binary number system and the hexadecimal number systems. This chapter will cover arithmetic. There will be a review of converting numbers to powers of ten form and vice-versa. There will be a review of adding, subtracting, multiplying and dividing powers of ten numbers. Students will develop an understanding of how to use powers of ten and scientific notation in order to manage very large and very small numbers.

Any field of technology will involve the use of fractions, decimal numbers, and percent. In technology we often deal with expressions or equations that may contain fractions or deal with numbers that are non-whole numbers. In this chapter we will review how to add, subtract, multiply and divide real number fractions. Additionally, we will learn how to convert between fractions, decimals, and percent. Students will learn how to compute ratios and solve percentage error calculations.

7.2 DECIMAL NUMBER SYSTEM

Decimal means ten. In the decimal number system there are ten items. These items are called *digits*. The ten digits are 0, 1, 2, 3, 4, 5, 6, 7, 8, and 9. Zero has the least value. Nine has the greatest value. An additional count causes a *carry*. The carry is equal to 10 and is said to occupy the tens position and the 0 possesses the units position. The process continues each time 9 is reached in the units' position. When a 9 appears in the tens position, the next carry to the tens position produces a carry to the hundreds position. Figure 7-1 below, shows the names for places up to millions.

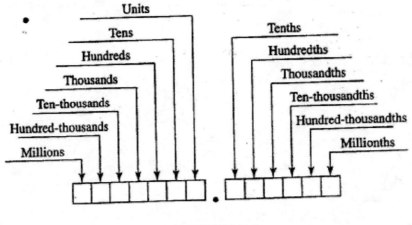

FIGURE 7-1

Remember that a 1 in the tens position possesses a value that is 10 times that of a 1 in the units position. This philosophy is true for each position of greater weight. Thus, the decimal numbering system has 10 as its base.

7.3 SIGNIFICANT DIGITS

Significant digits are all the digits from 1 to 9. Zero is significant only when it changes the value of a number. Other words, zero is significant except when in the leftmost position. Significant digits are independent of the decimal points.

Example 7-1

How many significant digits exist in 125?

SOLUTION

The decimal is located to the right of 5.

125.000

All three digits are significant because they are left of the decimal point.

Example 7-2

How many significant digits exist in 0546?

SOLUTION

There are three significant digits present. The zero in the leftmost position is not significant because it does not change the value of the number.

Example 7-3

How many significant digits exist in 6440?

SOLUTION

There are four significant digits present. The zero in the rightmost position is significant because it changes the value of the number.

Example 7-4

How many significant digits exist in 7.4?

SOLUTION

Both numbers are significant.

Example 7-5

How many significant digits exist in 0.613582?

SOLUTION

There are six significant digits present. The zero is not significant.

Example 7-6

How many significant digits exist in 0.005432?

SOLUTION

There are four significant digits present. None of the zeros are significant.

7.4 ROUNDING WHOLE NUMBERS

In problem solving it is common practice to simplify numbers with many digits. This simplification can be accomplished by replacing nonzero digits with zeros. For example, 83,248 could be *rounded-off* to 83,250 to the nearest ten; 83,200 to the nearest hundred; 83,000 to the nearest thousand; or 80,000 to the nearest ten-thousand. This process of simplification is called *rounding* or *rounding-off*. In Electronics if the *rounder* (digit used to round-off a number) is greater than or equal to 5, then we round up the number to the next higher digit.

Rounding-off numbers makes problem solving less difficult. Some accuracy is lost as a result of rounding off. The more rounding-off we do the less accurate the number. In Electronics, we work with components that normally have 5% or 10% tolerances. We usually, make measurements with instruments whose tolerances are within the 5% or 10% range.

Let's inspect 83,248 again. When we rounded-off to the nearest ten, we rounded-off to 83,250. We had the choice of rounding down to 83,240 or rounding up to 83,250. The digit 8 is the one that is rounding the whole number in the case of the nearest ten. The digit 8 is the *rounder*. Since 8 is larger than 5, we rounded 83,248 to 83,350. When rounding-off to the nearest hundred, the *rounder* is 4. Since 4 is less than 5, we rounded 83,248 to 83,200. When rounding-off to the nearest thousand, the *rounder* is 2. Since 2 is less than 5, we rounded 83,248 to 83,000. When rounding-off to the nearest ten- thousand, the *rounder* is 3. Since 3 is less than 5, we rounded 83,248 to 80,000. Remember that although the digit 5 could indicate up or down, in Electronics it is typically rounded up.

7.5 ROUNDING NON-WHOLE NUMBERS

Non-whole numbers are rounded by using the same rules as for whole numbers. As with whole numbers, we work from the least significant to the most significant digits.

Example 7-7

Consider the number 934.762.

Round-off to the nearest:

a) tenth
b) hundredth
c) ones (units)
d) tens
e) hundreds

SOLUTION

a) The digit 6 is the one that is rounding the non-whole number in the case of the nearest tenth. Thus digit 6 is the *rounder*. Since 6 is larger than 5, we should round 934.762 to 934.800. The final expression could be written as 934.8, since the last two zeros are not significant.

b) When rounding-off to the nearest hundredth, the *rounder* is 2. Since 2 is less than 5, we should round 934.762 to 934.760. The final expression could be written as 934.76, since the last zero is not significant.

c) When rounding-off to the nearest ones (units), the *rounder* is 7. Since 7 is greater than 5, we should round 934.762 to 935.000. The final expression could be written as 935, since the last three zeros are not significant.

d) When rounding-off to the nearest tens, the *rounder* is 4. Since 4 is less than 5, we should round 934.762 to 930.000. The zero preceding the decimal is significant and thus cannot be dropped. However, the three zeros following the decimal are not significant and can be dropped. The final expression could be written as 930.

e) When rounding-off to the nearest hundreds, the *rounder* is 3. Since 3 is less than 5, we should round 934.762 to 900.000. The two zeros preceding the decimal are significant and thus cannot be dropped. However, the three zeros following the decimal are not significant and can be dropped. The final expression could be written as 900.

7.6 SIGNED NUMBERS DEFINED

In mathematics, numbers may be either positive (+) or negative (-). The plus sign is not usually written.   If we saw the numbers 3, -2, -8, and 7 written, we would acknowledge that the numbers 3 and 7 are positive and the numbers 2 and 8 are negative.

Figure 7-2 shows a straight line that starts at zero and extends both left and right. Notice that numbers starting at zero and extending to the right are positive. Numbers starting at zero and extending to the left are negative. The symbol < means *less than*. The symbol > means *greater than*.

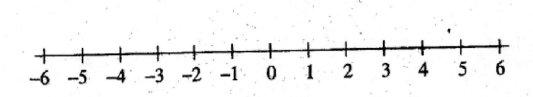

FIGURE 7-2

In comparing signed numbers, the rightmost number is the greater and the leftmost number is the lesser. For example, compare 5 and –6. We could say that 5 is greater than –6 (5 > -6), or we could say that –6 is less than 5 (-6 < 5).

Consider the numbers –8, -4 and 2. We could say that –8 < -4 < 2. In other words, we could say that 2 > -4 > -8. Notice that in comparing –4 and –8 we said that –4 > -8. Remember, on the number scale –4 is to the right of –8. This indicates that –4 is greater than –8. –4 is more positive than –8. –8 is more negative than –4.

Compare the numbers 6 and 1. We could say that 1 is more negative than 6. Thus, mathematically 1 < 6.
We could say that 6 is more positive than 1.Thus, mathematically 6 > 1.

The absolute value of a number is that number without regard to sign. The absolute value of +3 and –3 is 3 and is symbolized as |3|. This indicates that no matter whether 3 is – or +, the distance from the origin (0) is 3.

12

7.7 ADDITION AND SUBTRACTION

In Addition to using the symbols to represent the sign of a number, we can use these symbols to denote the operations of Addition and Subtraction.

To add numbers with like signs, add the numbers and affix the sign to the answer.

Example 7-8

Find the total sum of the following numbers:

a) $7 + 5 + 8$

b) $-7 + (-3) + (-2)$

c) $-7 - 3$

SOLUTION

a) $7 + 5 + 8 = 20$

b) $-(7 + 3 + 2) = -12$

c) $-7 - 3 = (-7) + (-3) = -(7 + 3) = -10$

To add numbers with unlike signs, subtract the smaller from the larger and attach the sign of the larger to the answer.

Example 7-9

Find the total sum of the following numbers:

a) $(-5) + 2$

b) $(-1) + 6$

c) $(-2) + 8 + (-7)$

SOLUTION

a) $-(5-2) = -3$

b) $+(6-1) = 5$

c) $(-2) + 8 + (-7) = -(7+2) + 8 = -(9) + 8 = -(9-8) = -1$

In Subtraction, we call the first number the *minuend*. The second number is the *subtrahend*. The answer is the *difference*. To subtract, change the sign of the *subtrahend* and then add, following the rule for addition. The equation for the difference is written as equation 4-1.

Minuend – Subtrahend = difference   (4-1)

Example 7-10

What is the difference, if -3 is subtracted from -1?

SOLUTION

$-1 - (-3) = -1 + 3 = 2$

7.8 MULTIPLICATION AND DIVISION

($\times$), ($\cdot$) and (*) are symbols used to indicate multiplication. The symbols ($\div$) and (/) are used to indicate division.

Figure 7-3 shows the names of each part of a multiplication or division.

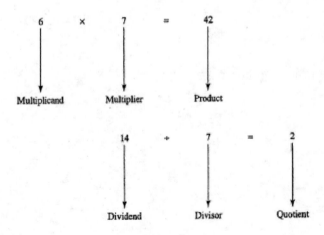

FIGURE 7-3

Common rules for multiplying and dividing signed numbers:

Rule 1: If all numbers are positive, then the answer is positive.

Rule 2: If there is an even number of negative signs, the answer is positive.

Rule 3: If there is an odd number of negative signs, the answer is negative.

Example 7-11

Perform the following operations:

1. $16 \times (-4)$

2. $(-12) * (-7)$

3. $10 \times 6 \times 2$

4. $45 \div 9$

5. $-36 \div (-18)$

6. $-48 / 4$

7. $(-0.5) \cdot 2$

SOLUTION

1. $16 \times (-4) = -64$

2. $(-12) * (-7) = 84$

3. $10 \times 6 \times 2 = 120$

4. $45 \div 9 = 45 \times (1/9) = 5$

5. $-36 \div (-18) = (-36) \times (-\frac{1}{18}) = 2$

6. $-48 / 4 = -12$

7. $(-0.5) \cdot 2 = \left(-\frac{1}{2}\right) \cdot 2 = -1$

7.9 CONVERTING NUMBERS TO POWERS OF TEN FORM

In technology, we often work with very large numbers or very small numbers. *Powers of ten* or *scientific notation* make it easier to deal with these numbers. In Table 7-1, numbers that are 10 or multiples of 10 have been converted to powers of ten form. 10 is the *base* and *n* is the *exponent*.

TABLE 7-1

$$1 \times 10 = 10^1$$
$$10 \times 10 = 100 = 10^2$$
$$10 \times 10 \times 10 = 1000 = 10^3$$
$$10 \times 10 \times 10 \times 10 = 10,000 = 10^4$$
$$10 \times 10 \times 10 \times 10 \times 10 = 100,000 = 10^5$$
$$10 \times 10 \times 10 \times 10 \times 10 \times 10 = 1,000,000 = 10^6$$

.

.

.

$$10 \times 10 \times 10 \times 10, ..., 10 = 10^n$$

Let's look at $10 \times 10 \times 10 \times 10 \times 10 = 100,000 = 10^5$. In this expression 10^5, the number 10 is the *base* and 5 the *exponent*. When a multiple of 10 ten is represented like this, it is said to be in the powers of ten form. 10^5 is read "ten to the fifth power." The exponent tells us how many times 10 is used as a factor. The exponent also tells the number of zeros that are included to the right of the digit 1. Thus in 100,000, 10 is used as a factor 5 times ($10 \times 10 \times 10 \times 10 \times 10$) so the exponent is 5. Counting the number of zeros to the right of 1 in 100,000 we again get 5, which also tells us the exponent is 5. $100,000 = 10^5$.

In converting some multiple of 10 to powers of ten form, count the number of zeros. This number is the exponent. The answer is 10 raised to that power.

Example 7-12

Find the power of ten expression for 100,000,000.

SOLUTION

$$100,000,000 = 10 \times 10 \times 10 \times 10 \times 10 \times 10 \times 10 \times 10 = 10^8$$

7.10 CONVERTING FROM POWERS OF TEN FORM TO NUMBERS

We will now consider how to convert from powers of ten form to a number. Remember that the exponent tells us how many times 10 is used as a factor. The exponent tells us how many zeros follow the 1. For example, let's change 10^2 to a number. 10^2 is read "ten to the second power." 2 is the exponent. Therefore, 10 is multiplied by itself two times: $10 \times 10 = 100$. Again, this is the same as saying that the answer is 1 followed by two zeros. In converting from powers of ten form for numbers with positive exponents, write the digit 1 and follow with as many zeros as indicated by the exponent.

7.11 CONVERTING DECIMAL FRACTIONS TO POWERS OF TEN FORM

When we dealt with numbers that were multiples of 10, we learned that the exponents were 1 or greater. If the number is 1, the exponent is zero. $10^0 = 1$. There are no zeros following the number 1; therefore, in powers of ten form, the exponent is zero.

Numbers whose values are less than 1 have *negative* exponents. Table 7-2 below shows some of these numbers and their exponents. The exponent tells us how many places to the right of the decimal point the 1 is located.

TABLE 7-2

$$1 = 10^0$$
$$0.1 = 10^{-1}$$
$$0.01 = 10^{-2}$$
$$0.001 = 10^{-3}$$
$$0.0001 = 10^{-4}$$
$$0.00001 = 10^{-5}$$
$$0.000001 = 10^{-6}$$
$$0.0000001 = 10^{-7}$$

Table 7-3 shows the conversion of numbers to decimal fractions.

TABLE 7-3

$0.1 = \dfrac{1}{10}$	$0.01 = \dfrac{1}{100}$
$0.001 = \dfrac{1}{1000}$	$0.0001 = \dfrac{1}{10,000}$
$0.00001 = \dfrac{1}{100,000}$	$0.000001 = \dfrac{1}{1,000,000}$

Table 7-4 combines Table 7-2 and 7-3. It shows the relationship between negative powers of ten, decimal numbers, and decimal fractions.

TABLE 7-4

$$10^{-1} = 0.1 = \frac{1}{10} = \frac{1}{10^1}$$

$$10^{-2} = 0.01 = \frac{1}{100} = \frac{1}{10^2}$$

$$10^{-3} = 0.001 = \frac{1}{1000} = \frac{1}{10^3}$$

$$10^{-4} = 0.0001 = \frac{1}{10,000} = \frac{1}{10^4}$$

$$10^{-5} = 0.00001 = \frac{1}{100,000} = \frac{1}{10^5}$$

$$10^{-6} = 0.000001 = \frac{1}{1,000,000} = \frac{1}{10^6}$$

Example 7-13

Convert 10^{-8} to

a) decimal number
b) decimal fraction

SOLUTION

a)

0.00000001

b)

$$\frac{1}{100,000,000}$$

7.12 MULTIPLICATION IN POWERS OF TEN FORM

To multiply numbers in powers of ten form, add the exponents.

$$(10^n) \times (10^m) = 10^{(n+m)}$$

Example 7-14

Multiply the following numbers in powers of ten form:

a) $10^{-5} \times 10^4$

b) $10^{-2} \times 10^{-6}$

c) $10^1 \times 10^3$

SOLUTION

a) $10^{-5} \times 10^4 = 10^{(-5)+(4)} = 10^{-1}$

b) $10^{-2} \times 10^{-6} = 10^{(-2)+(-6)} = 10^{-8}$

c) $10^1 \times 10^3 = 10^{1+3} = 10^4$

7.13 DIVISION IN POWERS OF TEN FORM

To divide numbers in powers of ten form, subtract the exponents.

$$\frac{1}{10^n} = 10^{-n}$$

$$\frac{1}{10^{-n}} = 10^n$$

$$\frac{10^n}{10^m} = 10^{n-m}$$

Example 7-15

Divide the following numbers in powers of ten form:

a) $\dfrac{10^7}{10^{-3}}$

b) $\dfrac{10^{-2}}{10^4}$

c) $\dfrac{10^{-1}}{10^{-8}}$

d) $\dfrac{1}{0.0001}$

e) $\dfrac{1000}{0.001}$

SOLUTION

a) $\dfrac{10^7}{10^{-3}} = 10^{7-(-3)} = 10^{10}$

b) $\dfrac{10^{-2}}{10^4} = 10^{-2-(4)} = 10^{-6}$

c) $\dfrac{10^{-1}}{10^{-8}} = 10^{-1-(-8)} = 10^7$

d) $\dfrac{1}{0.0001} = \dfrac{1}{10^{-4}} = 10^4$

e) $\dfrac{1000}{0.001} = \dfrac{10^3}{10^{-3}} = 10^{(3-(-3))} = 10^6$

Example 7-16

Perform the indicated operations and express the answer in powers of ten form.

$$\frac{10^{-3} \times 10^{-2} \times 10^6}{10^{-2} \times 10^4}$$

SOLUTION

$$\frac{10^{-3} \times 10^{-2} \times 10^6}{10^{-2} \times 10^4} = \frac{10^{-3+(-2)+6}}{10^{-2+4}} = \frac{10^1}{10^2} = 10^{1-2} = 10^{-1}$$

7.14 COMVERTING BETWEEN REGULAR NUMBERS AND POWERS OF TEN NOTATION

Consider the number 1230. Let's convert the number to powers of ten notation with positive exponents.

$1230 = 123.0 \times 10^1 = 12.30 \times 10^2 = 1.230 \times 10^3 = 0.1230 \times 10^4 = 0.01230 \times 10^5$

This is the same as writing,

$1230 = 123.0 \times 10 = 12.30 \times 100 = 1.230 \times 1000 = 0.1230 \times 10,000 =$
$0.01230 \times 100,000$

For each place we move the decimal point left in a number, the exponent increases by 1. In other words, the exponent becomes more positive as the decimal point moves left.

Example 7-17

Change 356 to powers of ten form with an exponent of

a) 2
b) 4

SOLUTION

a)

$356 = 3.56 \times 10^2$. The exponent changes by 2 in a positive direction, so the decimal point moves 2 places to the left.

b)

$356 = 0.0356 \times 10^4$. The exponent changes by 4 in a positive direction, so the decimal point moves 4 places to the left.

Now let's consider the same number to powers of ten form with negative exponents.

Consider the number 1230. Let's convert the number to powers of ten notation with positive exponents.

$1230 = 12,300 \times 10^{-1} = 123,000 \times 10^{-2} = 1,230,000 \times 10^{-3} = 12,300,000 \times 10^{-4}$

As we move the decimal point right, the exponent becomes more negative. For each place we move the point right, the exponent decreases by 1 (becomes more negative).

$1230 = 12,300 \times 10^{-1}$

$12,300 \times 10^{-1} = 123,000 \times 10^{-1+(-1)} = 123,000 \times 10^{-2}$

$123,000 \times 10^{-2} = 1,230,000 \times 10^{-2+(-1)} = 1,230,000 \times 10^{-3}$

For each place we move the decimal point right in a number, the exponent decreases by one. In other words, as we make the exponent more negative, the decimal point moves right.

Example 7-18

Change 72.3 to powers of ten form with an exponent of

a) -1
b) -3

SOLUTION

a)

$72.3 = 723 \times 10^{-1}$. The exponent changes by 1 in a negative direction, so the decimal point moves 1 place to the right.

b)

72.3 = 72,300 × 10^{-3}. The exponent changes by 3 in a negative direction, so the decimal point moves 3 places to the right.

7.15 EXPRESSING NUMBERS IN SCIENTIFIC NOTATION AND ENGINEERING NOTATION

Two means for writing large or small numbers are using scientific notation and engineering notation. The scientific notation method is for general use in working with numbers. Engineering notation is very useful when working with numbers in electricity.

In engineering and technology it is common practice to round answers to two, three, or four significant digits and then to change the number to a number between 1 and 10 times some power of ten. When numbers are written in this form, they are in scientific notation. Scientific notation is writing numbers using powers of ten and maintaining one digit to the left of the decimal. The exponent is whatever value is required to indicate the correct decimal position. The following numbers are written in scientific notation:

2.67×10^3 1.204×10^{-6} -1.16×10^{-1} 1.00×10^9 1.23×10^{-2}

Example 7-19

Express the number 1204 in Scientific Notation and rounded to three places.

SOLUTION

$1204 = 1.204 \times 10^3$

We must move the decimal point three places left in order to have a number between 1 and 10. That will make the exponent 3.

Now let's round off to three places. The rounder is 4. Since 4 is less than 5, we round down the number.

The final answer is 1.20×10^3.

Example 7-20

Express the number 0.00007508 in Scientific Notation and rounded to three places.

SOLUTION

$0.00007508 = 7.508 \times 10^{-5}$

We must move the decimal point five places right in order to have a number between 1 and 10. That will make the exponent -5.

Now let's round off to three places. The rounder is 8. Since 8 is greater than 5, we round up the number to the next higher digit.

The final answer is 7.51×10^{-5}.

Example 7-21

Write the following numbers in Scientific Notation:

a) 234,570,000,000,000

b) 0.000000100972

c) 4,683.8

d) 0.05871

SOLUTION

a) $234,570,000,000,000 = 2.3457 \times 10^{14}$

b) $0.000000100972 = 1.00972 \times 10^{-7}$

c) $4,683.8 = 4.68 \times 10^{3}$

d) $0.05871 = 5.871 \times 10^{-2}$

As mentioned earlier in this chapter, great accuracy in problem solving is not practical in Electronics because we work with electrical components whose values are given to two significant digits. It is possible that actual and theoretical results may differ by as much as ±

10%. It is common in the electronics field to round off to three significant digits, even though most hand calculators do give eight or more.

Engineering notation is using powers of ten in which the exponent is always a multiple of three.

Example 7-22

Write the following numbers in Engineering Notation:

a) 234,561,000,000,000

b) 4,783

c) 0.0000000822

SOLUTION

a) $234,561,000,000,000 = 234 \times 10^{12}$

b) $4,783 = 4.783 \times 10^{3}$

c) $0.0000000822 = 82.2 \times 10^{-9}$

7.16 POWERS AND ROOTS IN BASE TEN

When raising a power to a power, multiply the exponents.

Example 7-23

Perform the following operations:

a) $(10^{-2})^{-3}$

b) $\left(\dfrac{1}{10^{3}}\right)^{3}$

SOLUTION

a) $(10^{-2})^{-3} = 10^{-2 \times -3} = 10^{6}$

b) $\left(\dfrac{1}{10^{3}}\right)^{3} = \dfrac{1^{3}}{10^{3 \times 3}} = \dfrac{1}{10^{9}} = 10^{-9}$

7.17 SQUARE AND CUBE ROOTS OF POWERS OF TEN

To find the square root of powers of ten, we multiply the exponent by $\sqrt{}$ or $\dfrac{1}{2}$.

To find the cube root of powers of ten, we multiply the exponent by $\sqrt[3]{}$ or $\dfrac{1}{3}$.

Example 7-24

For the given power of ten, find:

$$\left(\dfrac{1}{10^{2}}\right)$$

a) square root of powers of ten.
b) cube root of powers of ten.

SOLUTION

a) $\sqrt{\dfrac{1}{10^{2}}} = \left(\dfrac{1}{10^{2}}\right)^{\frac{1}{2}} = \dfrac{1^{\frac{1}{2}}}{10^{2 \times \frac{1}{2}}} = \dfrac{1}{10^{1}} = \dfrac{10^{0}}{10^{1}} = 10^{0-1} = 10^{-1}$

b) $\sqrt[3]{\dfrac{1}{10^{2}}} = \left(\dfrac{1}{10^{2}}\right)^{\frac{1}{3}} = \dfrac{1^{\frac{1}{3}}}{10^{2 \times \frac{1}{3}}} = \dfrac{1}{10^{\frac{2}{3}}} = \dfrac{10^{0}}{10^{\frac{2}{3}}} = 10^{0-\frac{2}{3}} = 10^{-\frac{2}{3}}$

Example 7-25

For the given power of ten, find:

10^4

a) square root of powers of ten.
b) cube root of powers of ten.

SOLUTION

a) $\sqrt{10^4} = \left(10^4\right)^{\frac{1}{2}} = 10^{\frac{4 \times 1}{2}} = 10^{\frac{4}{2}} = 10^2$

b) $\sqrt[3]{10^4} = \left(10^4\right)^{\frac{1}{3}} = 10^{\frac{4 \times 1}{3}} = 10^{\frac{4}{3}}$

7.18 RECIPROCALS

The reciprocal of a number is that number divided into 1. $\frac{1}{3}$ is the reciprocal of 3. $\frac{1}{50}$ is the reciprocal of 50.

Example 7-26

Find the reciprocal of 350×10^2. Express your answer in Scientific Notation rounded to three places.

SOLUTION

$$\text{Reciprocal} = \frac{1}{350 \times 10^2} = \frac{1}{35000} = 2.8571 \times 10^{-5}$$

Now round off to three places.

7 is the rounder. Since 7 is greater than 5, the final answer is 2.86×10^{-5}.

7.19 BASIC ARITHMETIC OPERATIONS

We can add or subtract numbers in power of ten or when using Scientific Notation provided the exponents are the same. Exponents do not have to be the same when multiplying or dividing numbers in powers of ten.

Rule 1: $(A \times 10^n) \pm (B \times 10^n) = (A \pm B) \times 10^n$

Rule 2: $(A \times 10^n)(B \times 10^m) = (A)(B) \times 10^{n+m}$

Example 7-27

Find the sum of $6,300 + 75,000$ as a power of 10.

SOLUTION

$$
\begin{aligned}
6,300 + 75,000 &= (6.3 \times 1000) + (75 \times 1000) \\
&= (6.3 \times 10^3) + (75 \times 10^3) \\
&= (6.3 + 75) \times 10^3 \\
&= 81.3 \times 10^3
\end{aligned}
$$

Example 7-28

Find the difference of $0.00096 - 0.000086$ as a power of 10.

SOLUTION

$$
\begin{aligned}
0.00096 - 0.000086 &= (96 \times 0.00001) - (8.6 \times 0.00001) \\
&= (96 \times 10^{-5}) - (8.6 \times 10^{-5}) \\
&= (96 - 8.6) \times 10^{-5} \\
&= 87.4 \times 10^{-5}
\end{aligned}
$$

Example 7-29

Find the product of $(0.0002) \times (0.00007)$ as a power of 10.

SOLUTION

$$
\begin{aligned}
(0.0002) \times (0.00007) &= [(2) \times (0.0001)] \times [(7) \times (0.00001)] \\
&= (2 \times 10^{-4}) \times (7 \times 10^{-5}) \\
&= (2 \times 7) \times (10^{-4} \times 10^{-5}) \\
&= (2 \times 7) \times 10^{(-4 + -5)} \\
&= 14 \times 10^{-9}
\end{aligned}
$$

7.20 PRIME NUMBERS AND PRIME FACTORS

A number that has no whole-number factors except 1 and itself is called a *prime number*. Some examples of prime numbers are 2, 3, 5, 7, and 11. A number that is not prime is divisible by more than one prime number. For example, 4, 6, 8, 9, and 10 are not prime numbers because they are all divisible by more than one prime number. 4 is divisible by 2; 6 is divisible by 2 or 3, and so on. The prime numbers that make up a nonprime number are called *prime factors*. In determining prime factors, we ignore 1 as a factor.

Example 7-30

What are the prime factors of 10, 15, 21, and 26?

SOLUTION

$10 = 2 \cdot 10$

$15 = 3 \cdot 5$

$21 = 3 \cdot 7$

$26 = 2 \cdot 13$

Example 7-31

What are the prime factors of 8, 9, 36, and 150?

SOLUTION

$8 = 2 \cdot 2 \cdot 2 = 2^3$

$9 = 3 \cdot 3 = 3^2$

$36 = 2 \cdot 2 \cdot 3 \cdot 3 = 2^2 \cdot 3^2$

$150 = 2 \cdot 3 \cdot 5 \cdot 5 = 2 \cdot 3 \cdot 5^2$

7.21 WHAT IS A FRACTION?

Fraction is a number that expresses part of a group. Fractions are written in the form a/b or $\frac{a}{b}$, where **a** and **b** are whole numbers, and the number **b** is not zero. The number **a** is called the

numerator, and the number **b** is called the denominator. The following numbers are all fractions:
$1/2$, $\frac{3}{7}$, $6/10$, $\frac{6}{99}$.

Fractions have been reduced to lowest term when there are no common factors in the numerator and denominator. To reduce fractions to lowest terms, we first find the prime factors of the numerator and denominator and then cancel the common factors.

Example 7-32

Write a fraction that represents the portion of the pie that is shaded.

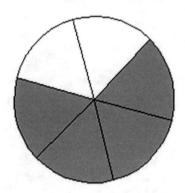

SOLUTION

There are 6 pieces in the group, and 4 of them are shaded. 6 is the denominator. 4 is the numerator. The fraction 4/6 represents the shaded portion of the circle below. We can now reduce the fraction to its lowest terms. As seen from the bottom, we can cancel 2 from the numerator and denominator.

$$\frac{4}{6} = \frac{2 \times 2}{2 \times 3} = \frac{2}{3}$$

The shaded portion represents $\frac{2}{3}$ of the pie.

Example 7-33

If possible reduce the following fractions to the lowest terms:

a) $\frac{4}{5}$

b) $\frac{12}{21}$

c) $\dfrac{39}{45}$

d) $\dfrac{48}{96}$

SOLUTION

a) $\dfrac{4}{5} = \dfrac{2 \times 2}{5}$

There are no common factors, so the fraction is already in lowest terms.

b) $\dfrac{12}{21} = \dfrac{2 \times 2 \times 3}{3 \times 7} = \dfrac{2 \times 2 \times \cancel{3}}{\cancel{3} \times 7} = \dfrac{2 \times 2}{7}$

There is a common factor of 2 that will cancel out in both the numerator and denominator.

$\dfrac{4}{7}$ is the lowest term.

c) $\dfrac{39}{45} = \dfrac{3 \times 13}{3 \times 3 \times 5} = \dfrac{\cancel{3} \times 13}{\cancel{3} \times 3 \times 5} = \dfrac{13}{3 \times 5} = \dfrac{13}{15}$

There is a common factor of 3 that will cancel out in both the numerator and denominator.

$\dfrac{13}{15}$ is the lowest term.

d) $\dfrac{48}{96} = \dfrac{2 \times 2 \times 2 \times 2 \times 3}{2 \times 2 \times 2 \times 2 \times 2 \times 3} = \dfrac{\cancel{2} \times \cancel{2} \times \cancel{2} \times \cancel{2} \times \cancel{3}}{\cancel{2} \times \cancel{2} \times \cancel{2} \times \cancel{2} \times 2 \times \cancel{3}} = \dfrac{1}{2}$

There are four common factors of 2 that will cancel out in both the numerator and denominator. There is a common factor of 3 that will cancel out in both the numerator and denominator.

$\dfrac{1}{2}$ is the lowest term.

7.22 MULTIPLICATION OF FRACTIONS

To multiply fractions, we must first multiply the numerators and second multiply the denominators. We can cancel like factors in order to reduce to the lowest terms.

Example 7-34

Find the product of the following fractions and reduce to lowest terms:

a) $\dfrac{1}{8} \times \dfrac{1}{2}$

b) $\dfrac{2}{3} \times \dfrac{3}{10}$

c) $\dfrac{4}{21} \times \dfrac{3}{5} \times \dfrac{5}{8}$

d) $\dfrac{2}{5} \times \dfrac{1}{6}$

SOLUTION

a) $\dfrac{1}{8} \times \dfrac{1}{2} = \dfrac{1}{16}$

b) $\dfrac{2}{3} \times \dfrac{3}{10} = \dfrac{6}{30} = \dfrac{6}{5 \times 6} = \dfrac{\cancel{6}}{5 \times \cancel{6}} = \dfrac{1}{5}$

There is a common factor of 6 that will cancel out in both the numerator and denominator.

c) $\dfrac{4}{21} \times \dfrac{3}{5} \times \dfrac{5}{8} = \dfrac{60}{840} = \dfrac{2 \times 2 \times 3 \times 5}{2 \times 2 \times 2 \times 3 \times 5 \times 7} = \dfrac{\cancel{2} \times \cancel{2} \times \cancel{3} \times \cancel{5}}{\cancel{2} \times \cancel{2} \times 2 \times \cancel{3} \times \cancel{5} \times 7} = \dfrac{1}{2 \times 7} = \dfrac{1}{14}$

There are two common factors of 2 that will cancel out in both the numerator and denominator. There is a common factor of 3 that will cancel out in both the numerator and denominator. There is a common factor of 5 that will cancel out in both the numerator and denominator.

d) $\dfrac{2}{5} \times \dfrac{1}{6} = \dfrac{2}{30} = \dfrac{2}{2 \times 3 \times 5} = \dfrac{\cancel{2}}{\cancel{2} \times 3 \times 5} = \dfrac{1}{15}$

There is a common factor of 2 that will cancel out in both the numerator and denominator.

7.23 DIVISION OF FRACTIONS

From arithmetic we learned that when we divide fractions we simply invert the divisor and multiply.

Example 7-35

Perform the indicated divisions and reduce answers to the lowest terms.

a) $\dfrac{7}{8} \div \dfrac{3}{5}$

b) $\dfrac{1}{3} \div \dfrac{2}{5}$

c) $\dfrac{9}{16} \div \dfrac{189}{200}$

d) $\dfrac{3}{7} \div 4$

SOLUTION

a) $\dfrac{7}{8} \div \dfrac{3}{5} = \dfrac{7}{8} \times \dfrac{5}{3} = \dfrac{35}{24}$

b) $\dfrac{1}{3} \div \dfrac{2}{5} = \dfrac{1}{3} \times \dfrac{5}{2} = \dfrac{5}{6}$

c) $\dfrac{9}{16} \div \dfrac{189}{200} = \dfrac{9}{16} \times \dfrac{200}{189} = \dfrac{1800}{3024} = \dfrac{2 \times 2 \times 2 \times 3 \times 3 \times 5 \times 5}{2 \times 2 \times 2 \times 2 \times 3 \times 3 \times 3 \times 7}$

$= \dfrac{\cancel{2} \times \cancel{2} \times \cancel{2} \times \cancel{3} \times \cancel{3} \times 5 \times 5}{\cancel{2} \times \cancel{2} \times \cancel{2} \times 2 \times \cancel{3} \times \cancel{3} \times 3 \times 7} = \dfrac{5 \times 5}{2 \times 3 \times 7} = \dfrac{25}{42}$

There are three common factors of 2 that will cancel out in both the numerator and denominator. There are two common factors of 3 that will cancel out in both the numerator and denominator.

d) $\dfrac{3}{7} \div 4 = \dfrac{3}{7} \times \dfrac{1}{4} = \dfrac{3}{28}$

7.24 ADDITION AND SUBTRACTION OF FRACTIONS

Two or more fractions can be combined into one when the denominators are identical. When the denominators of fractions are identical, that number is the common denominator.

When adding fractions, your first step is to determine if the denominators are identical. If they are, the next step is to add the numerators, and reduce to lowest terms.

Example 7-36

Perform the following additions and reduce to lowest terms:

a) $\dfrac{3}{8} + \dfrac{1}{8}$

b) $\dfrac{4}{11} + \dfrac{3}{11} + \dfrac{2}{11}$

SOLUTION

a) $\dfrac{3}{8} + \dfrac{1}{8} = \dfrac{4}{8} = \dfrac{2 \times 2}{2 \times 2 \times 2} = \dfrac{2 \times 2}{2 \times 2 \times 2} = \dfrac{1}{2}$

b) $\dfrac{4}{11} + \dfrac{3}{11} + \dfrac{2}{11} = \dfrac{9}{11}$

When subtracting fractions, your first step is to determine if the denominators are identical. If they are, the next step is to subtract the smaller numerator from the larger numerator and attach the sign of the larger numerator to the fraction.

We don't leave fractions with negative numerators or denominators if we can avoid it. We change the signs so that the fraction in the answer is either positive or negative and both numerator and denominator are positive. Any two signs of a fraction may be changed without changing the value of the fraction.

For example, $\dfrac{-3}{8}$ can be rewritten as $-\dfrac{3}{8}$.

Likewise, $\dfrac{-3}{-8}$ can be rewritten as $\dfrac{3}{8}$.

Furthermore, $\dfrac{3}{-8}$ can be rewritten as $-\dfrac{3}{8}$.

Lastly, $-\dfrac{-3}{-8}$ can be rewritten as $-\dfrac{3}{8}$.

Example 7-37

Perform the indicated operation and reduce to lowest terms:

$$\frac{10}{12} - \frac{1}{12}$$

SOLUTION

$$\frac{10}{12} - \frac{1}{12} = \frac{9}{12} = \frac{3 \times 3}{2 \times 2 \times 3} = \frac{3}{4}$$

When the fractions we are adding or subtracting have unlike denominators, we cannot add them directly as before. We must find a common denominator. Once we have a common denominator, we can add and subtract as before.

Example 7-38

Perform the indicated operations:

a) $\dfrac{1}{4} + \dfrac{1}{6}$

b) $\dfrac{6}{35} - \dfrac{3}{14}$

c) $\dfrac{7}{12} + \dfrac{5}{8} - \dfrac{5}{6}$

d) $\dfrac{1}{3} + \dfrac{1}{4} + \dfrac{1}{5}$

SOLUTION

a) $\dfrac{1}{4} + \dfrac{1}{6} = \dfrac{3 \times 1}{12} + \dfrac{2 \times 1}{12} = \dfrac{5}{12}$

b)

$\dfrac{6}{35} - \dfrac{3}{14} = \dfrac{14 \times 6}{490} - \dfrac{35 \times 3}{490} = \dfrac{84}{490} - \dfrac{105}{490} = -\dfrac{21}{490} = -\dfrac{3 \times 7}{2 \times 5 \times 7 \times 7} = -\dfrac{3 \times 7}{2 \times 5 \times 7 \times 7} = -\dfrac{3}{2 \times 5 \times 7} = -\dfrac{3}{70}$

c) $\dfrac{7}{12} + \dfrac{5}{8} - \dfrac{5}{6} = \dfrac{2 \times 7}{24} + \dfrac{3 \times 5}{24} - \dfrac{4 \times 5}{24} = \dfrac{14}{24} + \dfrac{15}{24} - \dfrac{20}{24} = \dfrac{9}{24} = \dfrac{3 \times 3}{2 \times 2 \times 2 \times 3} = \dfrac{3 \times 3}{2 \times 2 \times 2 \times 3} = \dfrac{3}{8}$

d) $\dfrac{1}{3} + \dfrac{1}{4} + \dfrac{1}{5} = \dfrac{20 \times 1}{60} + \dfrac{15 \times 1}{60} + \dfrac{12 \times 1}{60} = \dfrac{20}{60} + \dfrac{15}{60} + \dfrac{12}{60} = \dfrac{47}{60}$

7.25 IMPROPER FRACTIONS AND MIXED NUMBERS

When the numerator is greater than the denominator, the fraction is called an *improper fraction*. Some examples are $\dfrac{5}{4}$, $\dfrac{7}{2}$, and $\dfrac{25}{12}$. Improper fractions always have a value greater than 1.

Numbers that have a whole-number part and a fractional part are called *mixed numbers*. Some examples are $4\dfrac{2}{3}$, $7\dfrac{1}{4}$, and $2\dfrac{3}{4}$. When we write $4\dfrac{2}{3}$, we are really saying that we have 4 plus $\dfrac{2}{3}$: $4 + \dfrac{2}{3}$. Although we do not write the "+", we understand that it is there.

Example 7-39

Convert $\dfrac{4}{3}$ to a mixed number.

SOLUTION

Perform the indicated division. Write the remainder as a fraction.

$$
\begin{array}{r}
1+\dfrac{1}{3} \\[2ex]
3\,\overline{\smash{)}\,4} \\[1ex]
\dfrac{3}{1}
\end{array}
$$

Example 7-40

Change $2\dfrac{2}{3}$ to an improper fraction.

SOLUTION

Multiply the whole number and the denominator of the fraction.

$2 \times 3 = 6$

Add the numerator of the fraction to this number.

$6 + 2 = 8$

This number is the numerator in the answer. The denominator is unchanged.

$$2\dfrac{2}{3} = \dfrac{6+2}{3} = \dfrac{8}{3}$$

7.26 MULTIPLICATION AND DIVISION OF IMPROPER FRACTIONS

Multiplying and dividing improper fractions is no different from multiplying and dividing proper fractions. When the answer is an improper fraction, we change it to a mixed number.

Example 7-41

Perform the indicated operation. If the final answer is an improper fraction, convert it to a mixed number.

a) $2\dfrac{1}{3} \times 3\dfrac{7}{8}$

b) $\dfrac{5}{3} \times 2$

c) $\dfrac{8}{3} \div \dfrac{1}{4}$

SOLUTION

a) $2\dfrac{1}{3} \times 3\dfrac{7}{8} = \dfrac{7}{3} \times \dfrac{31}{8} = \dfrac{217}{24} = 9\dfrac{1}{24}$

b) $\dfrac{5}{3} \times 2 = \dfrac{5}{3} \times \dfrac{2}{1} = \dfrac{10}{3} = 3\dfrac{1}{3}$

c) $\dfrac{8}{3} \div \dfrac{1}{4} = \dfrac{8}{3} \times \dfrac{4}{1} = \dfrac{32}{3} = 10\dfrac{2}{3}$

7.27 ADDITION AND SUBTRACTION OF IMPROPER FRACTIONS

To add and subtract, we change all mixed numbers to improper fractions and perform the additions and subtractions as we did with proper fractions.

Example 7-42

Perform the indicated operations. Express your answers as mixed numbers or as proper fractions.

a) $\dfrac{16}{9} + \dfrac{4}{3}$

b) $3\dfrac{1}{3} + \dfrac{8}{15}$

c) $4\dfrac{2}{5} - 2\dfrac{1}{10}$

d) $\dfrac{9}{7} + \dfrac{8}{3} - 1\dfrac{2}{3}$

SOLUTION

a) $\dfrac{16}{9} + \dfrac{4}{3} = \dfrac{16}{9} + \dfrac{3 \times 4}{9} = \dfrac{16}{9} + \dfrac{12}{9} = \dfrac{28}{9} = 3\dfrac{1}{9}$

b) $3\dfrac{1}{3} + \dfrac{8}{15} = \dfrac{10}{3} + \dfrac{8}{15} = \dfrac{5 \times 10}{15} + \dfrac{8}{15} = \dfrac{50}{15} + \dfrac{8}{15} = \dfrac{58}{15} = 3\dfrac{13}{15}$

c) $4\dfrac{2}{5} - 2\dfrac{1}{10} = \dfrac{22}{5} - \dfrac{21}{10} = \dfrac{2 \times 22}{10} - \dfrac{21}{10} = \dfrac{44}{10} - \dfrac{21}{10} = \dfrac{23}{10} = 2\dfrac{3}{10}$

d) $\dfrac{9}{7} + \dfrac{8}{3} - 1\dfrac{2}{3} = \dfrac{9}{7} + \dfrac{8}{3} + \dfrac{5}{3} = \dfrac{3 \times 9}{21} + \dfrac{7 \times 8}{21} - \dfrac{7 \times 5}{21} = \dfrac{27}{21} + \dfrac{56}{21} - \dfrac{35}{21} = \dfrac{48}{21} = 2\dfrac{6}{21}$

$= 2\dfrac{3 \times 2}{3 \times 7} = 2\dfrac{\cancel{3} \times 2}{\cancel{3} \times 7} = 2\dfrac{2}{7}$

7.28 DECIMALS

When working with fractions, it is often desirable or necessary to express answers as decimal numbers rather than as mixed numbers. Emphasis was placed on decimals in Chapter 1.

Example 7-43

Add the mixed numbers: $3\dfrac{1}{4}$ and $2\dfrac{1}{6}$, express the answer as a decimal rounded off to three places.

SOLUTION

$3\dfrac{1}{4} + 2\dfrac{1}{6} = \dfrac{13}{4} + \dfrac{13}{6} = \dfrac{3 \times 13}{12} + \dfrac{2 \times 13}{12} = \dfrac{39}{12} + \dfrac{26}{12} = \dfrac{65}{12} = 65 \div 12 = 5.4166 = 5.42$

7.29 THE PERCENT

A percent is a ratio of a number to 100. A percent can be expressed using the percent symbol %. For example, 10 percent or 10% are both the same, and stand for the ratio 10:100.

A percent is equivalent to a fraction with denominator 100. For instance, 5% of something is the same as 5/100 of that thing.

Example 7-44

$2\frac{1}{2}\%$ is equal to what fraction?

SOLUTION

$$2\frac{1}{2}\% = \frac{5}{2} \div 100 = \frac{5}{2} \times \frac{1}{100} = \frac{5}{200} = \frac{1}{40}$$

Example 7-45

52% most nearly equals which one of the following 1/2, 1/4, 2, 8, or 1/5?

SOLUTION

$52\% = \frac{52}{100}$. This is very close to $\frac{50}{100}$, or $\frac{1}{2}$.

Example 7-46

$\frac{13}{25}$ is what %?

SOLUTION

We want to convert $\frac{13}{25}$ to a fraction with 100 in the denominator:

$$\frac{13}{25} = \frac{13 \times 4}{25 \times 4} = \frac{52}{100} = 52\%.$$

Percent and hundredths are basically equivalent. This makes conversion between percent and decimals very easy. To convert from a decimal to a percent, just move the decimal 2 places to the right. For example, 0.15 = 15 hundredths = 15%.

Example 7-47

Convert the decimal 0.0006 to percent (%).

SOLUTION

$0.0006 \times 100 = 0.06\%$

Converting from percent to decimal form is similar, only you move the decimal point 2 places to the left. You must also be sure, before doing this, that the percentage itself is expressed in decimal form, without fractions.

Example 7-48

Express 3% in decimal form.

SOLUTION

Moving the decimal 2 to the left (and adding in 0's to the left of the 3 as place holders) we get 0.03.

Express $97\frac{1}{4}\%$ in decimal form. First we write $97\frac{1}{4}$ in decimal form: 97.25. Then we move the decimal 2 places to the left to get 0.9725, so $97\frac{1}{4}\% = 0.9725$. This makes sense, since $97\frac{1}{4}\%$ is nearly 100%, and 0.9725 is nearly 1.

When estimating percent, it is helpful to remember the fractional equivalent of some simple percent.

$100\% = 1$
(100% of any number equals that number.)

$50\% = 1/2 = 0.5$
(50% of any number equals half of that number.)

$25\% = 1/4 = 0.25$
(25% of any number equals one-fourth of that number.)

10% = 1/10 = 0.1
(10% of any number equals one-tenth of that number.)

1% = 1/100 = 0.01
(1% of any number equals one-hundredth of that number.)

Because it is very easy to switch between a decimal and a percent, estimating a percent is as easy as estimating a fraction as a decimal, and converting to a percent by multiplying by 100.

Example 7-49

Estimate 13% of 72.

SOLUTION

Twice 13% is 26%, which is very close to 25%, and 25%=1/4. We may multiply both sides by 1/2 to get an estimate for 13%: $13\% \cong 12.5\% = 1/2 \times 25\% = 1/2 \times 1/4 = 1/8$. Using our estimate of 1/8 for 13%, $1/8 \times 72 = 9$, so we get an estimate of 9 for 13% of 72.

If we had calculated this exactly, 13% of 72 equals 9.36. It may look like we did a lot more work to get the estimate of 9 that just multiplying 72 by 0.13, but with practice, keeping in mind some simple percent and the fractions they are equal to will enable you to estimate some number combinations very quickly.

7.30 FRACTION TO DECIMAL TO PERCENTAGE CONVERSIONS

Numbers are expressed as fractions, decimal numbers, or percentages. In this section, we will convert both fractions and decimals to their percent equivalents.

To change a fraction to a percentage, we must first change the fraction to a decimal number, and then change the decimal number to a percentage.

To change a decimal number to a percent, multiply by 100 and add the % sign.

Example 7-50

Change the following fractions to percentages. Round the decimal numbers to three places if the fourth place number is not zero.

a) $\dfrac{3}{4}$

b) $\dfrac{7}{25}$

c) $\dfrac{11}{12}$

d) $\dfrac{47}{100}$

SOLUTION

a) $\dfrac{3}{4} = 0.75$

     $0.75 \times 100 = 75.0\%$

b) $\dfrac{7}{25} = 0.280$

     $0.280 \times 100 = 28.0\%$

c) $\dfrac{11}{12} = 0.9167$

     $0.9167 \times 100 = 91.67\%$

d) $\dfrac{47}{100} = 0.470$

     $0.470 \times 100 = 47.0\%$

To change from a percent to a fraction we must first change from a percent to a decimal number and then convert the decimal number to a fraction. To change from a percent to a decimal number, divide the number by 100 and remove the % sign.

Example 7-51

Change the following percentages to fractions.

a) 30%
b) 6.25%

c) 52%
d) 162.5%

SOLUTION

a) 30%

$$\frac{30\%}{100} = 0.3$$

$$0.3 = \frac{30}{100} = \frac{3}{10}$$

b) 6.25%

$$\frac{6.25\%}{100} = 0.0625$$

$$0.0625 = \frac{625}{1000} = \frac{1}{16}$$

c) 52%

$$\frac{52\%}{100} = 0.52$$

$$0.52 = \frac{52}{100} = \frac{13}{25}$$

d) 162.5%

$$\frac{162.5\%}{100} = 1.625$$

$$1.625 = \frac{1625}{1000} = \frac{15}{8}$$

Example 7-52

There are 16 games scheduled in a regular football season. Suppose that the Atlanta Falcons won 13 games and lost only 3 games.

a) What percentage of games did they win?

b) What percentage of games did they lose?

SOLUTION

a) $\dfrac{13}{16} \times 100 = 0.8125 \times 100 = 81.25\%$

b) $\dfrac{3}{16} \times 100 = 0.1875 \times 100 = 18.75\%$

7.31 PERCENTAGE ERROR

A percentage error is used in Electronics to compare the accuracy of calculated and measured values.

$$\% \text{ error} = \frac{|\text{Calculated Value} - \text{Measured Value}|}{|\text{Calculated Value}|} \times 100\%$$

Example 7-53

Calculate the % error of a resistor that has a calculated value of 20 and measured value of 19.

SOLUTION

$$\% \text{ error} = \frac{|20 - 19|}{|20|} \times 100\% = |0.05| \times 100 = 5\%$$

7.32 RATIO

A ratio is quotient of two quantities. It can be considered as an expression of the relative magnitude of one quantity to another and is generally in the form of a fraction.

Example 7-54

A classroom consists of thirty children. There are 10 boys and 20 girls.

a) What is ratio of boys to girls?

b) What is ratio of girls to boys?

c) What is the ratio of children who are boys?

d) What is the ratio of children who are girls?

SOLUTION

a) $\dfrac{10}{20} = \dfrac{1}{2}$

b) $\dfrac{20}{10} = \dfrac{2}{1} = 2$

c) $\dfrac{10}{30} = \dfrac{1}{3}$

c) $\dfrac{20}{30} = \dfrac{2}{3}$

7.33 SPECIAL APPLICATION OF PERCENTAGES

7.33.1 INTEREST

Interest is a fee paid to borrow money. It is usually charged as a percent of the total amount borrowed. The percent charged is called the interest rate. The amount of money borrowed is called the principal. There are two types of interest, simple interest and compound interest.

7.33.2 SIMPLE INTEREST

Simple interest is interest figured on the principal only, for the duration of the loan. Figure the interest on the loan for one year, and multiply this amount by the number of years the money is borrowed for.

7.33.3 COMPOUND INTEREST

Compound interest is interest figured on the principal and any interest owed from previous years. The interest charged the first year is just the interest rate times the amount of the loan. The interest charged the second year is the interest rate, times the sum of the loan and the interest from the first year. The interest charged the third year is the interest rate, times the sum of the loan and the first two years' interest amounts. Continue figuring the interest in this way for any additional years of the loan.

Example 7-55

A bank charges 7% interest on a $1000 loan. How much interest will the borrower have to pay each year the money is borrowed.

SOLUTION

It will cost the borrower 7% of $1000, which is $70, for each year the money is borrowed. Note that when the loan is up, the borrower must pay back the original $1000.

Example 7-56

A bank charges 8% simple interest on a $600 loan, which is to be paid back in two years. What is the total charge for borrowing the money?

SOLUTION

It will cost the borrower 8% of $600, which is $48, for each year the money is borrowed. Since it is borrowed for two years, the total charge for borrowing the money will be $96. After the two years the borrower will still have to pay back the original $600.

Example 7-57

A bank charges 8% compound interest on a $600 loan, which is to be paid back in two years. What is the total charge for borrowing the money?

SOLUTION

It will cost the borrower 8% of $600 the first year, which is $48. The second year, it will cost 8% of $600 + $48 = $648, which is $51.84. The total amount of interest owed after the two years is $48 + $51.84 = $99.84. Note that this is more than the $96 that would be owed if the bank was charging simple interest as computed in Example 2-27.

Example 7-58

A bank charges 4% compound interest on a $1000 loan, which is to be paid back in three years. What is the total charge for borrowing the money?

SOLUTION

It will cost the borrower 4% of $1000 the first year, which is $40. The second year, it will cost 4% of $1000 + $40 = $1040, which is $41.60. The third year, it will cost 4% of $1040 + $41.60 = $1081.60, which is $43.26 (with rounding). The total amount of interest owed after the three years is $40 + $41.60 + 43.26 = $124.86.

7.33.4 PERCENT INCREASE AND DECREASE

Percent increase and decrease of a value measure how that value changes, as a percentage of its original value.

Example 7-59

A collectors' comic book is worth $120 in 1994, and in 1995 its value is $132. What is the percentage increase from 1994 to 1995?

SOLUTION

The change is $132 - $120 = $12, an increase in price of $12; since $12 is 10% of $120, we say its value increased by 10% from 1994 to 1995.

Example 7-60

A bakery makes a chocolate cake that has 8 grams of fat per slice. A new change in the recipe lowers the fat to 6 grams of fat per slice. What is the percentage decrease in fat?

SOLUTION

The change is 8g - 6g = 2g, a decrease of 2 grams; since 2 grams is 25% of 8, we say that the new cake recipe has 25% less fat, or a 25% decrease in fat.

Example 7-61

Lateesha is training for the 1500 meter run. When she started training she could run 1500 meters in 5 minutes and 50 seconds. After a year of practice her time decreased by 8%. How fast can she run the race now?

SOLUTION

Her old time was $5 \times 60 + 50 = 350$ seconds, and 8% of 350 is 28, so she can run the race in $350 - 28 = 322$ seconds (5 minutes and 22 seconds).

Example 7-62

A fishing magazine sells 110,000 copies each month. The company's president wants to increase the sales by 6%. How many extra magazines would they have to sell to reach this goal?

SOLUTION

This problem is easy, since it only asks for the change in sales: 6% of 110,000 equals 6,600 more magazines.

7.33.5 PERCENT DISCOUNT

A discount is a decrease in price, so percent discount is the percent decrease in price.

Example 7-63

Chocolate bars normally cost 80 cents each, but are on sale for 40 cents each. What is the new percent discount?

SOLUTION

$$\frac{40}{80} \times 100 = 50\%$$

The chocolate is on sale at a 50% discount.

Example 7-64

A compact disc that sells for $12 is on sale at a 20% discount. How much does the disc cost on sale?

SOLUTION

The amount of the discount is 20% of $12, which is $2.40, so the sale price is $12.00 - $2.40 = $9.60.

Example 7-65

Movie tickets sell for $8.00 each, but if you buy 4 or more you get $1.00 off each ticket. What percent discount is this?

SOLUTION

We figure $1 as a percentage of $8: $1.00/$8.00 × 100% = 12.5%, so this is a 12.5% discount.

7.34 SIMPLE ALGEBRAIC EQUATIONS

When algebraic terms or expressions are separated by an equals sign, the resulting algebraic statement is called an *equation*. In the simplest equations, the literal numbers are raised to the first power. These equations are called *linear* equations. If the literal numbers are raised to the second power, we have second-degree equations.

All linear equations can be solved provided there is only one unknown—one literal number. Ohm's law may be either linear or second-degree equations, depending on the variables used. E = IR is a linear equation. If two of the variables are known, we can solve for the third. $P = I^2R$ is a second-degree equation I is raised to the second power. These equations can be solved, again provided that there is only one unknown variable.

Algebraic expressions separated by an equals sign (=) are called equations. The equals sign implies that the expressions are equal. We will call the expression to the left of the equals sign the *left side* and the expression to the right of the equals sign the *right side*.

7.35 SOLVING LINEAR (1ST ORDER) EQUATIONS

We can perform any mathematical operation on one side of an equation, provided we perform the same operation on the other side. This means that we can make any change we want in the value of one side as long as we make the same change in the other side.
We can add, subtract, multiply, divide, square, and so on. We can perform any of these operations as long as we maintain the equality of sides.

In solving equations, we typically solve for some unknown value. In simple linear, there is only one unknown and only one value for that unknown.

In order to find the solution for both linear and second-degree equations:

   a. Clear all fractions (if any).
   b. Move all terms containing the unknown to one side and combine them into one term. It is usually preferable to move unknowns to the left side.
   c. Move all constants to the other side.
   d. Perform the operation or operations necessary to make the coefficient of the unknown equal to 1 (remember to perform this operation on both sides).

   e. Substitute the value of the unknown back into the original equation to verify solution.

Example 7-66

$x + 6 = 20$

Solve for x.

SOLUTION

We want the unknown variable, x, on the left side by itself. This can be done by subtracting 6 from both sides. $x + 6 - 6 = x$. Remember, if we subtract 6 from the left side, we must subtract 6 from the right side to maintain the equality on both sides.

$x + 6 - 6 = 20 - 6$

$x = 14$

Then we replace the unknown with its value and check for equality:

$x + 6 = 20$

$14 + 6 = 20$

$20 = 20$

Example 6-67

$z - 3 = 24$

Solve for z.

SOLUTION

$z - 3 + 3 = 24 + 3$ (add 3 to both sides)

$z = 27$

$27 - 3 = 24$

$24 = 24$

Example 6-68

$-3t = 21$

Solve for t.

SOLUTION

$-3t = 21$

$\dfrac{-3t}{-3} = \dfrac{21}{-3}$ (Divide both sides by 4.)

$t = -7$

$-3(-7) = 21$

$21 = 21$

In this example, the left-side term is $-3t$. Since we have to find the value of t, we must somehow get rid of the -3. That is, we want the left side to equal t. We can make the left side equal to t by dividing by negative 3. But if we divide the left side by -3 we must also divide the right side by -3.

Example 6-69

$$\frac{y}{5} = 60$$

Solve for y.

SOLUTION

How can we make the left side equal to y? Multiplication by 5 is the only way it can be done.

$$\frac{y}{5} \times 5 = \frac{y5}{5} = y$$

Solving the equation for y, we get

$$\frac{y}{5} = 60$$

$$\frac{y}{5} \times 5 = 60 \times 5$$

$$y = 300$$

$$\frac{300}{5} = 60$$

$$60 = 60$$

Examples 7-68 and 7-69 show how we can move parts from one side to another by multiplying or dividing. A shortcut method of multiplying or dividing terms in order to simplify the terms is called cross-multiplication. When we cross-multiply, we multiply the numerator of one term and the denominator of the other term. Consider Example 7-69 again. (We have shown the 1 in the denominator of the right side just to help you see the process.

$$\frac{y}{5} = \frac{60}{1} \quad \text{If we cross-multiply, we get}$$

$$y \cdot 1 = 60 \cdot 5$$

$$y = 300$$

Cross-multiplication in this example is really the multiplication of both sides by 5 and then by 1.

Often the process can be done by inspection. It's a quick way of getting rid of a fraction when it is part of the equation.

Example 7-70

$$\frac{45}{a} = 5$$

Solve for a.

SOLUTION

We must get a out of the denominator. There are two ways we can do this. The first way is to take the reciprocal of both sides:

$$\frac{45}{a} = \frac{5}{1}$$

$$\frac{a}{45} = \frac{1}{5}$$

Next we multiply both sides by 45. This is the only way we can move 45 to the right side.

$$\frac{a}{45} \times 45 = \frac{1}{5} \times 45$$

$$\frac{45a}{45} = \frac{45}{5}$$

$$a = 9$$

Check: $\dfrac{45}{9} = 5$

$$5 = 5$$

The other way to solve the problem is to multiply both sides by a.

$$\frac{45}{a}(a) = 5a$$

$$\frac{45a}{a} = 5a$$

$45 = 5a$

Next we divide both sides by 5.

$$\frac{45}{5} = \frac{5a}{5}$$

$a = 9$

Example 7-71

$\frac{c}{3} = -5$ Find c.

SOLUTION

$\frac{c}{3}(3) = -5(3)$ (Multiply both sides by 3.)

$c = -15$

Check: $\frac{-15}{3} = -5$

$-5 = -5$

Example 7-72

$\frac{24}{-f} = -2$ Find f.

SOLUTION

$\frac{-f}{24} = -\frac{1}{2}$ (Take the reciprocal of both sides.)

$$\frac{-f}{24}(24) = -\frac{1}{2}(24)$$

$-f = -12$

$f = 12$ (Change the sign of both sides.)

Check: $\dfrac{24}{-12} = -2$

$\qquad -2 = -2$

Example 7-73

$\dfrac{2d}{5} = \dfrac{3}{4}$ Find d.

SOLUTION

$2d \cdot 4 = 3 \cdot 5$ (cross-multiply)

$8d = 15$

$d = \dfrac{15}{8} = 1\dfrac{7}{8}$ (Divide both sides by 8 and reduce to lowest terms.)

Example 7-74

$15 = 3rs$

Solve for each of the variables

 SOLUTION

Find r

$\dfrac{15}{3s} = \dfrac{3rs}{3s}$ (Divide both sides by 3s.)

$\dfrac{5}{s} = r$

$$r = \frac{5}{s}$$

Check: $15 = 3\left(\dfrac{5}{s}\right)s$

$$15 = \frac{3 \times 5 \times s}{s}$$

$$15 = 15$$

Find s

$$\frac{15}{3r} = \frac{3rs}{3r} \quad \text{(Divide both sides by } 3r.\text{)}$$

$$\frac{5}{r} = s$$

$$s = \frac{5}{r}$$

Check: $15 = 3\left(\dfrac{5}{r}\right)r$

$$15 = \frac{3 \times 5 \times r}{r}$$

$$15 = 15$$

7.36 SECOND-DEGREE EQUATIONS

The square root of the square of a number is that number. The square of the square root of a number is that number.

Example 7-75

$$e^2 = 81$$

Find e.

SOLUTION

$e^2 = 81$

$\sqrt{e^2} = \sqrt{81}$

$e = 9$

Example 7-76

$\sqrt{b} = 5$

Find b.

SOLUTION

We need b where we have $\sqrt{b}$. We must square the term to get rid of the square root.

$$\left(\sqrt{b}\right)^2 = b \quad \text{or} \quad \left(b^{\frac{1}{2}}\right)^2 = b^1 = b$$

We must also square the right side.

$\sqrt{b} = 5$

$\left(\sqrt{b}\right)^2 = 5^2$

$b = 5$

Check: $\sqrt{25} = 5$, $\qquad 5 = 5$

Example 7-77

$\dfrac{g^2}{4} = 16$

Find g

SOLUTION

$$\frac{g^2}{4}(4) = 16(4) \quad \text{(Multiply both sides by 4)}$$

$$g^2 = 64$$

$$\sqrt{g^2} = \sqrt{64}$$

$$g = 8$$

Check: $\dfrac{8^2}{4} = 16, \quad 16 = 16$

Example 7-78

$$\frac{\sqrt{j}}{2} = 3$$

Find j

SOLUTION

$$\frac{\sqrt{j}}{2} \times 2 = 3 \times 2 \quad \text{(Multiply both sides by 2.)}$$

$$\sqrt{j} = 6$$

$$j = 36 \quad \text{(square both sides)}$$

Check: $\dfrac{\sqrt{36}}{2} = 3$

$$\frac{6}{2} = 3$$

$$3 = 3$$

Example 7-79

$$4 = \frac{1}{3h\sqrt{m}}$$

a) Solve for the variable h.

b) Solve for the variable m.

SOLUTION

a) Find h.

$$4(h) = \frac{1}{3h\sqrt{m}}(h) \quad \text{(Multiply by } h\text{)}$$

$$4h = \frac{1}{3\sqrt{m}}$$

$$\frac{4h}{4} = \frac{1}{3\sqrt{m}}\left(\frac{1}{4}\right) \quad \text{(divide by 4)}$$

$$h = \frac{1}{12\sqrt{m}}$$

Check: $4 = \dfrac{1}{3\left(\dfrac{1}{12\sqrt{m}}\right)\left(\sqrt{m}\right)} = \dfrac{1}{3\left(\dfrac{1}{12}\right)} = \dfrac{1}{\dfrac{3}{12}} = \dfrac{12}{3} = 4$

b) Find m.

$$4\left(\sqrt{m}\right) = \frac{1}{3h\sqrt{m}}\left(\sqrt{m}\right) \quad \text{(multiply by } \sqrt{m}\text{)}$$

$$\frac{4\sqrt{m}}{4} = \frac{1}{3h}\left(\frac{1}{4}\right) \quad \text{(divide by 4)}$$

$$\sqrt{m} = \frac{1}{12h}$$

$$\left(\sqrt{m}\right)^2 = \left(\frac{1}{12h}\right)^2 \quad \text{(square both sides)}$$

$$m = \frac{1}{144h^2}$$

$$m = \frac{a^{-2}}{144}$$

Check: $4 = \dfrac{1}{3h\left(\dfrac{1}{12}h\right)} = \dfrac{1}{\dfrac{3h}{12h}} = \dfrac{12}{3} = 4$

7.37 APPLICATIONS

Algebra allows us to set up equations in order to solve problems. The next four examples are simple algebraic equations based on applications.

Example 7-80

$E = IR$

Find I when $E = 12$ V and $R = 12$ kΩ.

SOLUTION

$E = IR$

$\dfrac{E}{R} = \dfrac{IR}{R}$ (divide by R)

$\dfrac{E}{R} = I$

$I = \dfrac{E}{R}$ (change sides so that the unknown is on the left side)

Now plug in the values of E and R and solve.

$$I = \frac{12\text{ V}}{12 \times 10^3 \text{ }\Omega} = 1 \times 10^{-3} \text{ A} = 1 \text{ mA}$$

Example 7-81

$$P = \frac{E^2}{R}$$

Find E when P = 300 mW and R = 1.5 kΩ.

SOLUTION

Solve for E.

$$PR = \frac{E^2}{R}(R) \quad \text{(multiply both sides by R)}$$

$$PR = E^2$$

$$\sqrt{PR} = \sqrt{E^2} \quad \text{(take the square root of both sides)}$$

$$\sqrt{PR} = E$$

$$E = \sqrt{PR}$$

Plug in the known values.

$$E = \sqrt{\left(\left(300 \times 10^{-3} \text{ W}\right) \times \left(1.5 \times 10^3 \text{ }\Omega\right)\right)} = \sqrt{450} = 21.2 \text{ V}$$

Example 7-82

$$\frac{N_P}{N_S} = \sqrt{\frac{Z_P}{Z_S}} \quad \text{Find } Z_P \text{ when } Z_S = 8 \text{ }\Omega, N_P = 500, \text{ and } N_S = 25$$

SOLUTION

Solve for Z_P.

$$\left(\frac{N_P}{N_S}\right)^2 = \left[\sqrt{\frac{Z_P}{Z_S}}\right]^2 \quad \text{(square both sides)}$$

$$\left(\frac{N_P}{N_S}\right)^2 = \frac{Z_P}{Z_S}$$

$$\left(\frac{N_P}{N_S}\right)^2 \times Z_S = \frac{Z_P}{Z_S}(Z_S) \quad \text{(multiply both sides by } Z_S\text{)}$$

$$\left(\frac{N_P}{N_S}\right)^2 Z_S = Z_P$$

$$Z_P = \left(\frac{N_P}{N_S}\right)^2 Z_S$$

Plug in the known values.

$$Z_P = \left(\frac{500}{25}\right)^2 \times 8\,\Omega = 3200\,\Omega = 3.2\,k\Omega$$

Example 7-83

$$f_r = \frac{1}{2\pi\sqrt{LC}}$$

Find L if C = 400 pF and f_r = 15 kHz.

SOLUTION

Solve for L.

$$f_r \sqrt{LC} = \frac{1}{2\pi} \quad \text{(multiply by } f_r\text{)}$$

$$LC = \left(\frac{1}{2\pi f_r}\right)^2 \quad \text{(square both sides)}$$

$$LC = \frac{1}{\left(2\pi f_r\right)^2} \quad (1^2 = 1)$$

$$L = \frac{1}{\left(2\pi f_r\right)^2 C} \quad \text{(divide by C)}$$

Put in the known values.

$$L = \frac{1}{\left(2\pi \times 15{,}000 \text{ Hz}\right)^2 \times \left(400 \times 10^{-12}\right)} = \frac{1}{3.55} = 2.81 \times 10^{-1} \text{ H} = 281 \text{ mH}$$

7.38 SIMULTANEOUS LINEAR EQUATIONS

Every linear equation in two unknowns has an unlimited number of solutions. If we have two equations, each equation still has an unlimited number of solutions. However, if the two equations are plotted on the same system of rectangular coordinates, they will intersect at some common point provided they are not parallel lines and are not the same line. The coordinates of this common point of intersection, are said to be *simultaneous*.

7.38.1 GRAPHICAL SOLUTION

Example 7-84

Plot or graph the equations $x - 2y = 4$ and $3x + 2y = 4$ on the same system of rectangular coordinates. Find the coordinates of the point of intersection.

SOLUTION

The plot of the equations is shown in the Figure 7-4 below.

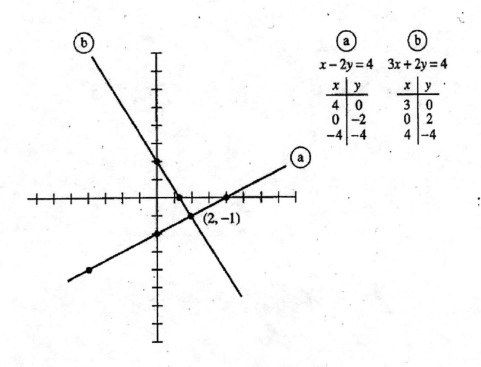

The table for equation (a):

a	
x − 2y = 4	
x	y
4	0
0	−2
−4	−4

The table for equation (b):

b	
3x + 2y = 4	
x	y
3	0
0	2
4	−4

(2, −1)

FIGURE 7-4

The point of intersection is (2,-1). This point is common to both equations. Because the lines intersect, there is a common solution, which in this case is (2,-1). Furthermore, this is the only solution. $x = 2$ and $y = -1$ are the only values common to both equations.

Example 7-85

Plot the following equations on the same system of rectangular coordinates. Find the coordinates of the point of intersection.

$x + y = 5$
$x - y = 3$

SOLUTION

The graph is shown in the Figure 7-5 below. The point of intersection is (4,1)

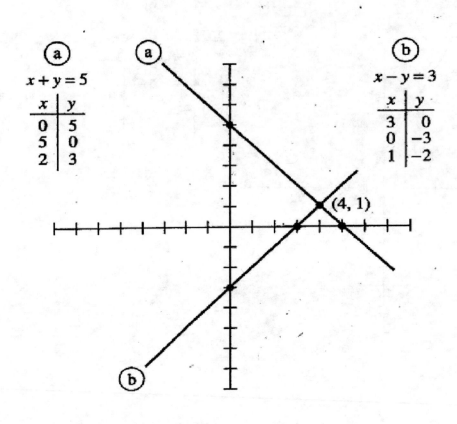

FIGURE 7-5

Example 7-86

Plot the following equations on the same system of rectangular coordinates. Find the coordinates of the point of intersection.

$x + y = 3$
$2x + y = 7$

SOLUTION

The graph is shown in the Figure 7-6 below. The point of intersection is (4,-1).

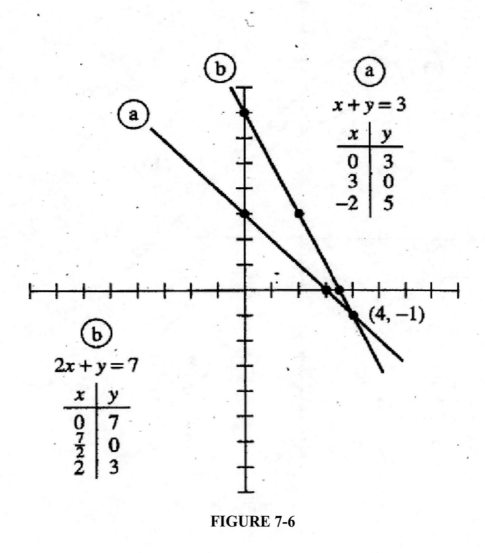

FIGURE 7-6

Example 7-87

Plot the following equations on the same system of rectangular coordinates. Find the coordinates of the point of intersection.

$x + 2y = 7$
$2x + 2y = 10$

SOLUTION

The graph is shown in the Figure 7-7 below. The point of intersection is (3,2).

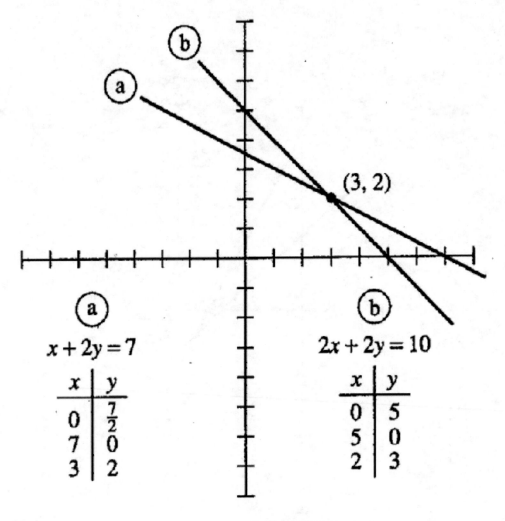

(3, 2)

<table>
<tr><th colspan="2">ⓐ
$x + 2y = 7$</th></tr>
</table>

ⓐ

$x + 2y = 7$

x	y
0	$\frac{7}{2}$
7	0
3	2

ⓑ

$2x + 2y = 10$

x	y
0	5
5	0
2	3

FIGURE 7-7

7.38.2 SOLUTION BY ALGEBRAIC ELIMINATION METHOD

In using the Algebraic Elimination method, we will change one or the other of the equations so that both x values, or both y values, have the same coefficient. If the signs of the coefficients are the same, we will subtract one equation from the other. If the signs are different, we will add the equations. The subtraction (or addition) results in a new equation that has only one unknown. We can now find the value of this unknown. This value is common to both original equations. The value of this unknown is then substituted back into the original equations and the other unknown, is then found.

Example 7-88

Solve for the unknown values (x_1, x_2) by using the Algebraic Elimination Method.

$$2x_1 + 2x_2 = -1 \quad (1)$$
$$3x_1 + 4x_2 = 5 \quad (2)$$

SOLUTION

First, let's eliminate the variable x_2.

Multiply equation (1) by -2 and then add the two equations.

$$-2[2x_1 + 2x_2 = -1] \rightarrow -4x_1 - 4x_2 = 2$$

$$\begin{aligned}
-4x_1 - 4x_2 &= 2 \\
+\ 3x_1 + 4x_2 &= 5 \\
\hline
-x_1 + 0x_2 &= 7
\end{aligned}$$

$$-x_1 = 7$$

$$x_1 = -7$$

Second, let's eliminate the variable x_1.

Multiply equation (1) by 3, multiply equation (2) by 2, and then subtract the two equations.

$$3[2x_1 + 2x_2 = -1] \rightarrow 6x_1 + 6x_2 = -3$$

$$2[3x_1 + 4x_2 = 5] \rightarrow 6x_1 + 8x_2 = 10$$

$$\begin{aligned}
6x_1 + 6x_2 &= -3 \\
-\ 6x_1 + 8x_2 &= 10 \\
\hline
0x_1 - 2x_2 &= -13
\end{aligned}$$

$$-2x_2 = -13$$

$$\frac{-2x_2}{-2} = \frac{-13}{-2}$$

$$x_2 = \frac{13}{2}$$

Example 7-89

Solve for the unknown values (x_1, x_2) by using the Algebraic Elimination Method.

$4x_1 + 2x_2 = 4$ (1)
$3x_1 + 3x_2 = 1$ (2)

SOLUTION

First, let's eliminate the variable x_2.

Multiply equation (1) by 3, multiply equation (2) by 2, and then subtract the two equations.

$3[4x_1 + 2x_2 = 4] \rightarrow 12x_1 + 6x_2 = 12$

$2[3x_1 + 3x_2 = 1] \rightarrow 6x_1 + 6x_2 = 2$

$$\begin{array}{r} 12x_1 + 6x_2 = 12 \\ - \ 6x_1 + 6x_2 = \ \ 2 \\ \hline 6x_1 + 0x_2 = 10 \end{array}$$

$6x_1 = 10$

$$\frac{6x_1}{6} = \frac{10}{6}$$

$$x_1 = \frac{5}{3}$$

Second, let's eliminate the variable x_1.

Multiply equation (1) by 3, multiply equation (2) by 4, and then subtract the two equations.

$3[4x_1 + 2x_2 = 4] \rightarrow 12x_1 + 6x_2 = 12$

$4[3x_1 + 3x_2 = 1] \rightarrow 12x_1 + 12x_2 = 4$

$$\begin{array}{r} 12x_1 + \ \ 6x_2 \ = 12 \\ - \ 12x_1 + 12x_2 \ = \ \ 4 \\ \hline 0x_1 \ - \ 6x_2 \ = \ \ 8 \end{array}$$

$-6x_2 = 8$

$$\frac{-6x_2}{-6} = \frac{8}{6}$$

$$x_2 = \frac{-4}{3}$$

7.38.3 SOLUTION BY SUBSTITUTION METHOD

This method involves finding the value of x (or y) in one equation and then substituting that value back into the other equation.

Example 7-90

Repeat Example 7-5 by using the Substitution Method.

$2x_1 + 2x_2 = -1$ (1)
$3x_1 + 4x_2 = 5$ (2)

SOLUTION

Solve equation (1) for x_2

$2x_1 - 2x_1 + 2x_2 = -1 - 2x_1$

$2x_2 = -1 - 2x_1$

$$\frac{2x_2}{2} = \frac{-1 - 2x_1}{2}$$

$$x_2 = \frac{-1 - 2x_1}{2} \quad (3)$$

Plug equation (3) into equation (2)

$$3x_1 + 4\left(\frac{-1 - 2x_1}{2}\right) = 5$$

Multiply the equation by 2 in order to eliminate the fraction.

$$\left(2 \times 3x_1\right) + \left(2 \times \left[4\left(\frac{-1 - 2x_1}{2}\right)\right]\right) = 5 \times 2$$

$6x_1 + 4(-1 - 2x_1) = 10$

$6x_1 - 4 - 8x_1 = 10$

$-2x_1 - 4 = 10$

$-2x_1 - 4 + 4 = 10 + 4$

$-2x_1 = 14$

$$\frac{-2x_1}{-2} = \frac{14}{-2} = -7$$

$x_1 = -7$

Plug x_1 into equation (3)

$$x_2 = \frac{-1 - 2(-7)}{2}$$

$$x_2 = \frac{13}{2}$$

Example 7-91

Repeat Example 7-89 by using the Substitution Method.

$4x_1 + 2x_2 = 4$ (1)

$3x_1 + 3x_2 = 1$ (2)

SOLUTION

Solve equation (2) for x_2

$3x_1 - 3x_1 + 3x_2 = 1 - 3x_1$

$3x_2 = 1 - 3x_1$

$$\frac{3x_2}{3} = \frac{1 - 3x_1}{3}$$

$$x_2 = \frac{1 - 3x_1}{3} \quad (3)$$

plug equation (3) into equation (1)

$$4x_1 + 2\left[\frac{1 - 3x_1}{3}\right] = 4$$

multiply the equation by 3 in order to eliminate the fraction

$$3 \cdot 4x_1 + 2 \cdot 3\left[\frac{1 - 3x_1}{3}\right] = 4 \cdot 3$$

$$12x_1 + 2[1 - 3x_1] = 12$$

$$12x_1 + 2 - 6x_1 = 12$$

$$6x_1 + 2 = 12$$

$$6x_1 + 2 - 2 = 12 - 2$$

$$6x_1 = 10$$

$$\frac{6x_1}{6} = \frac{10}{6}$$

$$x_1 = \frac{5}{3}$$

plug x_1 into equation (3)

$$x_2 = \frac{1 - 3\left(\frac{5}{3}\right)}{3} = \frac{1 - 5}{3}$$

$$x_2 = \frac{-4}{3}$$

7.39 MATRICES

A matrix is an ordered set of entries (elements) arranged rectangularly and set off by brackets. The entries can be variables or numbers. A matrix by itself has no particular value—it is merely a convenient method of representing a set of numbers.

The size of a matrix is given by the number of rows and columns, and nomenclature $m \times n$ is used for a matrix with m rows and n columns. For a *square matrix*, the number of rows and columns will be the same, a quantity known as the *order* of the matrix.

Uppercase letters are used to represent matrices, while lowercase letters represent the entries. For example, a_{23} would be the entry in the second row and third column of matrix A.

A *sub-matrix* is the matrix that remains when selected rows or columns are removed from the original matrix. For example, matrix Q is a sub-matrix of matrix A below.

$$A = \begin{bmatrix} a_{11} & a_{12} & a_{13} \\ a_{21} & a_{22} & a_{23} \\ a_{31} & a_{32} & a_{33} \end{bmatrix} \qquad Q = \begin{bmatrix} a_{11} & a_{13} \\ a_{31} & a_{33} \end{bmatrix}$$

An *augmented matrix* results when the original matrix is extended by repeating one or more of its rows or columns or by adding rows and columns from another matrix. The matrix B below is created by repeating the first and second column of the matrix A.

$$B = \begin{bmatrix} a_{11} & a_{12} & a_{13} & | & a_{11} & a_{12} \\ a_{21} & a_{22} & a_{23} & | & a_{21} & a_{22} \\ a_{31} & a_{32} & a_{33} & | & a_{31} & a_{32} \end{bmatrix}$$

7.39.1 SPECIAL TYPES OF MATRICES

Certain types of matrices are given by special designations.

A) Cofactor Matrix: a matrix with only one column

B) Column Matrix: a matrix with only one column

C) Complex Matrix: a matrix with complex number entries

D) Diagonal Matrix: a square matrix with all zero entries except a_{ij} for which $i = j$

E) Echelon Matrix: a matrix in which the number of zeros preceding the first nonzero entry of a row increases row by row until only zeros remain. A *row-reduced echelon matrix* in which the first nonzero entry in each row is a 1 and all other entries in the columns are zero.

F) Identity matrix: a diagonal (square) matrix with all nonzero entries equal to 1, usually designated as **I**, having the property that $\mathbf{AI} = \mathbf{IA} = \mathbf{A}$

G) Null Matrix: the same as a zero matrix

H) Row Matrix: a matrix with only one row

I) Scalar Matrix: a diagonal (square) matrix with all diagonal entries equal to some scalar k

J) Singular Matrix: a matrix whose determinant is zero

K) Skew Symmetric Matrix: a square matrix whose transpose is equal to the negative of itself (i.e., $\mathbf{A} = -\mathbf{A}^t$)

L) Square Matrix: a matrix with the same number of rows and columns (i.e., $m = n$)

M) Symmetrical Matrix: a square matrix whose transpose is equal to itself (i.e., $A^t = A$), which occurs only when $a_{ij} = a_{ji}$.

N) Triangular Matrix: a square matrix with zeros in all positions above or below the diagonal

O) Unit Matrix: the same as the identity matrix

P) Zero Matrix: a matrix with all zero entries.

Figure 7-8 shows some examples of special matrices.

Diagonal	Echelon	Row-reduced Echelon

$$
\begin{bmatrix} 9 & 0 & 0 & 0 \\ 0 & -6 & 0 & 0 \\ 0 & 0 & 1 & 0 \\ 0 & 0 & 0 & 5 \end{bmatrix}
\quad
\begin{bmatrix} 2 & 18 & 2 & 18 \\ 0 & 0 & 1 & 9 \\ 0 & 0 & 0 & 9 \\ 0 & 0 & 0 & 0 \end{bmatrix}
\quad
\begin{bmatrix} 1 & 9 & 0 & 0 \\ 0 & 0 & 1 & 0 \\ 0 & 0 & 0 & 1 \\ 0 & 0 & 0 & 0 \end{bmatrix}
$$

Identity	Triangular	Scalar

$$\begin{bmatrix} 1 & 0 & 0 & 0 \\ 0 & 1 & 0 & 0 \\ 0 & 0 & 1 & 0 \\ 0 & 0 & 0 & 1 \end{bmatrix} \quad \begin{bmatrix} 2 & 0 & 0 & 0 \\ 7 & 6 & 0 & 0 \\ 9 & 1 & 1 & 0 \\ 8 & 0 & 4 & 5 \end{bmatrix} \quad \begin{bmatrix} 3 & 0 & 0 & 0 \\ 0 & 3 & 0 & 0 \\ 0 & 0 & 3 & 0 \\ 0 & 0 & 0 & 3 \end{bmatrix}$$

FIGURE 7-8

7.39.2 ROW EQUIVALENT MATRICES

A matrix **B** is said to be row equivalent to a matrix **A** if it is obtained by a finite sequence of elementary row operations on **A**.

The finite sequence of elementary row operations includes:

i) interchanging the *ith* and *jth* rows

ii) multiplying the ith row by a nonzero scalar

iii) replacing the *ith* row by the sum of the original *ith* row and *k* times the *jth* row

7.40 GAUSS-JORDAN ELIMINATION METHOD

Gauss-Jordan elimination is the process of using these elementary row operations to row-reduce a matrix to echelon or row-reduced echelon forms. When a matrix has been converted to a row-reduced echelon matrix, it is said to be in row canonical form. Thus, the terms *row-reduced echelon form* and *row canonical form* are synonymous.

Example 7-92

Use Gauss-Jordan elimination method to solve the following system of simultaneous equations:

$2x + 3y - 4z = 1$

$3x - y - 2z = 4$

$4x - 7y - 6z = -7$

SOLUTION

The augmented matrix is created by appending the constant matrix to the coefficient matrix.

$$\begin{bmatrix} 2 & 3 & -4 & | & 1 \\ 3 & -1 & -2 & | & 4 \\ 4 & -7 & -6 & | & -7 \end{bmatrix}$$

Elementary row operations are used to reduce the coefficient matrix to canonical form. For example, two times the first row is subtracted from the third row. This step obtains the 0 needed in the a_{31} position.

$$\begin{bmatrix} 2 & 3 & -4 & | & 1 \\ 3 & -1 & -2 & | & 4 \\ 0 & -13 & 2 & | & -9 \end{bmatrix}$$

This process continues until the following form is obtained.

$$\begin{bmatrix} 1 & 0 & 0 & | & 3 \\ 0 & 1 & 0 & | & 1 \\ 0 & 0 & 1 & | & 2 \end{bmatrix}$$

$x = 3$, $y = 1$, and $z = 2$ satisfy this system of equations.

7.41 MINORS AND COFACTORS

Minors and cofactors are determinants of sub-matrices associated with particular entries in the original square matrix. The *minor* of entry a_{ij} is the determinant of a sub-matrix resulting from the elimination of the single row i and the single column j. For example, the minor corresponding to entry a_{12} in a 3×3 matrix A is the determinant of the matrix created by eliminating row 1 and column 2.

$$\text{minor of } a_{12} = \begin{vmatrix} a_{21} & a_{23} \\ a_{31} & a_{33} \end{vmatrix}$$

The cofactor of entry a_{ij} is the minor of a_{12} multiplied by either +1 or -1, depending on the position of the entry. (That is, the cofactor either exactly equals the minor or it differs only in sign.) The sign is determined according to the following positional matrix shown in Figure 7-9.

$$\begin{bmatrix} +1 & -1 & +1 & \cdots \\ -1 & +1 & -1 & \cdots \\ +1 & -1 & +1 & \cdots \\ \vdots & \vdots & \vdots & \end{bmatrix}$$

FIGURE 7-9

For example, the cofactor of entry a_{12} in matrix A is

$$\text{Cofactor of } a_{12} = -\begin{vmatrix} a_{21} & a_{23} \\ a_{31} & a_{33} \end{vmatrix}$$

Example 7-93 What is the cofactor corresponding to the -3 entry in the following matrix?

$$A = \begin{bmatrix} 2 & 9 & 1 \\ -3 & 4 & 0 \\ 7 & 5 & 9 \end{bmatrix}$$

SOLUTION

The minor's sub-matrix is created by eliminating the row and column of the -3 entry.

$$M = \begin{bmatrix} 9 & 1 \\ 5 & 9 \end{bmatrix}$$

The minor is the determinant of **M**:

det $(\mathbf{M}) = (9 \times 9) - (5 \times 1) = 76$

The sign corresponding to the -3 position is negative. Therefore, the cofactor is -76.

7.42 DETERMINANTS

A determinant is a scalar calculated from a square matrix. The determinant of matrix $\mathbf{A}$ can be represented as $D\{\mathbf{A}\}$, $Det\{\mathbf{A}\}$, $\Delta\mathbf{A}$, or $|\mathbf{A}|$.

The following rules can be used to simplify the calculation of determinants:

A) If $\mathbf{A}$ has a row or column of zeros, the determinant is zero.

B) If $\mathbf{A}$ has two identical rows or columns, the determinant is zero.

C) If $\mathbf{B}$ is obtained from $\mathbf{A}$ by adding a multiple of a row (column) to another row (column) in $\mathbf{A}$, then $|\mathbf{B}| = |\mathbf{A}|$.

D) If $\mathbf{A}$ is triangular, the determinant is equal to the product of the diagonal entries.

E) If $\mathbf{B}$ is obtained from $\mathbf{A}$ by multiplying one row or column in $\mathbf{A}$ by a scalar k, then $|\mathbf{B}| = k|\mathbf{A}|$.

F) If $\mathbf{B}$ is obtained from the n × n matrix $\mathbf{A}$ by multiplying by the scalar k, then $|k \times \mathbf{A}| = k^n|\mathbf{A}|$.

G) If $\mathbf{B}$ is obtained from $\mathbf{A}$ by switching two rows or columns in $\mathbf{A}$, then $|\mathbf{B}| = -|\mathbf{A}|$.

Calculation of determinants is laborious for all but the smallest or simplest of matrices. For a 2 ×2 matrix, the formula used to calculate the determinant is easy to remember. The determinant for the 2 ×2 matrix A is given by equation 7-1.

$$\mathbf{A} = \begin{bmatrix} a & b \\ c & d \end{bmatrix}$$

$$\det(A) = \begin{vmatrix} a & b \\ c & d \end{vmatrix} = ad - bc \quad (7\text{-}1)$$

Two methods are commonly used for calculating the determinant of 3 × 3 matrices by hand. The first one uses an augmented matrix constructed from the original matrix and the first two columns. The determinant is calculated as the sum of the products in the left-to-right downward diagonals less the sum of the products in the left-to-right upward diagonals. Figure 7-10 shows how to augment a 3 × 3 matrix. The determinant for the 3 ×3 matrix A is given by equation 7-2.

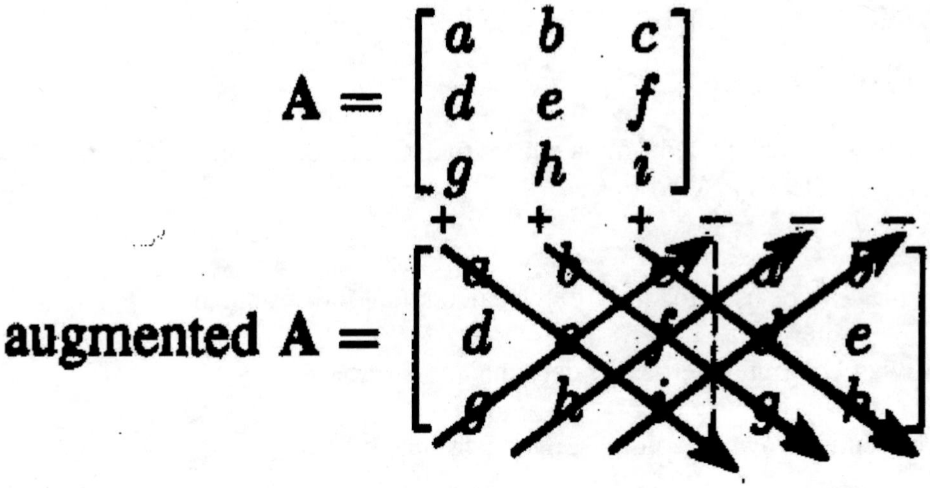

$$A = \begin{bmatrix} a & b & c \\ d & e & f \\ g & h & i \end{bmatrix}$$

augmented A =

FIGURE 7-10

$$\det(A) = aei - bfg + cdh - gec - hfa - idb \quad (7\text{-}2)$$

The second method of calculating the determinant is somewhat slower than the first for a 3 × 3 matrix but illustrates the method that must be used to calculate determinants of 4 × 4 and larger matrices. This method is known as the *expansion by cofactors*. One row (column) is selected as the base row (column). The selection is arbitrary, but the number of calculations required to obtain the determinant can be minimized by choosing the row (column) with the most zeros. The determinant is equal to the sum of the products of the entries in the base row (column) and their corresponding cofactors.

$$A = \begin{bmatrix} a & b & c \\ d & e & f \\ g & h & i \end{bmatrix}$$

$$\det(A) = a\begin{vmatrix} e & f \\ h & i \end{vmatrix} - d\begin{vmatrix} b & c \\ h & i \end{vmatrix} + g\begin{vmatrix} b & c \\ e & f \end{vmatrix}$$

Example 7-94

Calculate the determinant of matrix A by

a) cofactor expansion.

b) augmenting the matrix A.

$$A = \begin{bmatrix} 2 & 3 & -4 \\ 3 & -1 & -2 \\ 4 & -7 & -6 \end{bmatrix}$$

SOLUTION

a) Since there are no zero entries, it does not matter which row or column is chosen as base. Choose the first column.

$$\det(A) = 2\begin{vmatrix} -1 & -2 \\ -7 & -6 \end{vmatrix} - 3\begin{vmatrix} 3 & -4 \\ -7 & -6 \end{vmatrix} + 4\begin{vmatrix} 3 & -4 \\ -1 & -2 \end{vmatrix} = (2 \times (6\text{-}14)) -(3 \times (-18\text{-}28))+ (4 \times (-6\text{-}4)) = 82$$

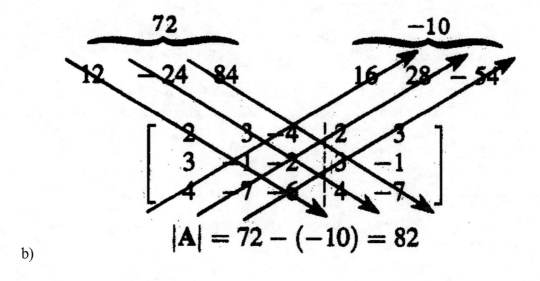

$$|A| = 72 - (-10) = 82$$

b)

7.43 SIMULTANEOUS EQUATIONS IN MATRIX FORM

$$ax_1 + bx_2 = b_1$$
$$cx_1 + dx_2 = b_2$$

$A \times X = b$ is the Matrix Form of the simultaneous equations.

$$A = \begin{bmatrix} a & b \\ c & d \end{bmatrix} \qquad X = \begin{bmatrix} x_1 \\ x_2 \end{bmatrix} \qquad b = \begin{bmatrix} b_1 \\ b_2 \end{bmatrix}$$

Coefficient Matrix	Variable Matrix	Constant Matrix
2×2 matrix	2×1 matrix	2×1 matrix

A is the coefficient matrix.
X is the variable matrix.
b is the Constant matrix.

The matrix size or address is given by $i \times j$.
i is the number of rows.
j is the number of columns.

Not all systems of simultaneous equations have solutions, and those that do may not have unique solutions. The existence of a solution can be determined by calculating the determinant of the coefficient matrix. These rules are summarized in Table 7-6.

Table 7-6
Solution Existence Rules for Simultaneous Equations

	$\mathbf{b} = 0$	$\mathbf{b} \neq 0$
det ($\mathbf{A}$) = 0	Infinite number of solution (linearly dependent equations)	Either an infinite number of solutions or no solution at all
det ($\mathbf{A}$) $\neq$ 0	Trivial solution only ($x_i = 0$)	Unique nonzero solution

If the system of linear equations is homogeneous (i.e., $\mathbf{b}$ is a zero matrix) and det ($\mathbf{A}$) is zero, there are an infinite number of solutions.

If the system is homogeneous and det ($\mathbf{A}$) is nonzero, only the trivial solution exists.

If the system of linear equations is non-homogeneous (i.e., $\mathbf{b}$ is not a zero matrix) and det ($\mathbf{A}$) is nonzero, there is a unique solution to the set of simultaneous equations.

If det ($\mathbf{A}$) is zero, a non-homogeneous system of simultaneous equations may still have a solution. The requirement is that the determinants of all substitutional matrices are zero, in which case there will be an infinite number of solutions. Otherwise, no solution exists.

Example 7-95

What is the size of the following matrix?

$$A = \begin{bmatrix} 7 & 8 \\ 1 & 0 \\ -2 & 1 \end{bmatrix}$$

SOLUTION

$i = 3$

$j = 2$

3×2 [matrix size]

Example 7-96

What is the size of the following matrix?

$$A = \begin{bmatrix} 2 & 1 & 3 \\ 6 & -3 & 0 \end{bmatrix}$$

SOLUTION

$i = 2$

$j = 3$

2×3 [matrix size]

Example 7-97

$10x_1 - 6x_2 = 7$
$5x_1 + 4x_2 = 9$

Find the A, x, and b matrices.

SOLUTION

$$A = \begin{bmatrix} 10 & -6 \\ 5 & 4 \end{bmatrix} \qquad x = \begin{bmatrix} x_1 \\ x_2 \end{bmatrix} \qquad b = \begin{bmatrix} 7 \\ 9 \end{bmatrix}$$

7.44 CRAMER'S RULE

Cramer's Rule uses determinants to find the solution to a set of simultaneous equations. Cramer's Rule is very popular tool to use in searching for the solution to equations in electrical and electronics circuits. Because Cramer's Rule is based on arithmetic instead of algebra, a solution is easier and quicker to obtain.

7.44.1 CRAMER'S RULE FOR SECOND-ORDER (2nd ORDER) DETERMINANTS

Another way to solve simultaneous equations is by using Cramer's Rule. This rule is based on using *determinants*. Determinants are arrays of numbers. These numbers correspond to the coefficients and constants of different equations.

$$Ax = b$$

$$A = \begin{bmatrix} a & b \\ c & d \end{bmatrix} \qquad x = \begin{bmatrix} x_1 \\ x_2 \end{bmatrix} \qquad b = \begin{bmatrix} b_1 \\ b_2 \end{bmatrix}$$

Determinant is a scalar that predicts whether or not a unique solution exists.

$|A| = ad - bc$

If $|A| = 0$, then a unique solution does not exist.

Equations 7-3 and 7-4 are used to compute the values of the 2 × 2 variable matrix.

$$x_1 = \frac{|A_1|}{|A|} \qquad (7\text{-}3)$$

$$x_2 = \frac{|A_2|}{|A|} \qquad (7\text{-}4)$$

A_1 and A_2 are called substitutional matrices. A_1 and A_2 are also called cofactor expansion matrices.

$$A_1 = \begin{bmatrix} b_1 & b \\ b_2 & d \end{bmatrix} \qquad A_2 = \begin{bmatrix} a & b_1 \\ c & b_2 \end{bmatrix}$$

Equations 7-5 and 7-6 are used to compute the determinants of the cofactor expansion matrices.

$$|A_1| = (b_1 \times d) - (b \times b_2) \qquad (7\text{-}5)$$

$$|A_2| = (a \times b_2) - (b_1 \times c) \qquad (7\text{-}6)$$

Example 7-98

Repeat Example 7-89 by using Cramer's Rule.

$2x_1 + 2x_2 = -1 \quad (1)$
$3x_1 + 4x_2 = 5 \quad (2)$

SOLUTION

$$A = \begin{bmatrix} 2 & 2 \\ 3 & 4 \end{bmatrix} \qquad x = \begin{bmatrix} x_1 \\ x_2 \end{bmatrix} \qquad b = \begin{bmatrix} -1 \\ 5 \end{bmatrix}$$

$$A_1 = \begin{bmatrix} -1 & 2 \\ 5 & 4 \end{bmatrix} \qquad A_2 = \begin{bmatrix} 2 & -1 \\ 3 & 5 \end{bmatrix}$$

Using equation 4-1 to compute the determinant yields:

$$|A| = (2 \times 4) - (2 \times 3) = 8 - 6 = 2$$

We will use equations 4-6 and 4-7 respectively in order to compute the determinants of the cofactor expansion matrices.

$$|A_1| = (-1 \times 4) - (2 \times 5) = -4 - 10 = -14$$

$$|A_2| = (2 \times 5) - (-1 \times 3) = 10 + 3 = 13$$

We will use equations 4-3 and 4-4 respectively in order to calculate the solution.

$$x_1 = \frac{|A_1|}{|A|} = \frac{-14}{2} = -7 \qquad x_2 = \frac{|A_2|}{|A|} = \frac{13}{2}$$

Example 7-99

Determine the solution set (x_1 and x_2) by using Cramer's Rule.

$$4x_1 + 2x_2 = 4 \quad (1)$$
$$3x_1 + 3x_2 = 1 \quad (2)$$

SOLUTION

$$A = \begin{bmatrix} 4 & 2 \\ 3 & 3 \end{bmatrix} \qquad x = \begin{bmatrix} x_1 \\ x_2 \end{bmatrix} \qquad b = \begin{bmatrix} 4 \\ 1 \end{bmatrix}$$

$$A_1 = \begin{bmatrix} 4 & 2 \\ 1 & 3 \end{bmatrix} \qquad A_2 = \begin{bmatrix} 4 & 4 \\ 3 & 1 \end{bmatrix}$$

Using equation 7-1 to compute the determinant yields:

$$|A| = (4 \times 3) - (2 \times 3) = 12 - 6 = 6$$

We will use equations 7-6 and 7-7 respectively in order to compute the determinants of the cofactor expansion matrices.

$$|A_1| = (4 \times 3) - (2 \times 1) = 12 - 2 = 10$$

$|A_2| = (4 \times 1) - (4 \times 3) = 4 - 3 = -8$

We will use equations 7-3 and 7-4 respectively in order to calculate the solution.

$$x_1 = \frac{10}{6} = \frac{5}{3}$$

$$x_1 = \frac{-8}{6} = \frac{-4}{3}$$

7.44.2 CRAMER'S RULE FOR THIRD-ORDER (3rd ORDER) DETERMINANTS

Let's now consider three equations and three unknowns. This determinant has three rows and three columns and is called a *third-order determinant*. Our general equations are as follows:

$a_1x + b_1y + c_1z = k_1$

$a_2x + b_2y + c_1z = k_2$

$a_3x + b_3y + c_3z = k_3$

Equations 7-7, 7-8, and 7-9 can be used to compute the solutions of x, y and z respectively.

$$x = \frac{\begin{bmatrix} k_1 & b_1 & c_1 \\ k_2 & b_2 & c_2 \\ k_3 & b_3 & c_3 \end{bmatrix}}{\begin{bmatrix} a_1 & b_1 & c_1 \\ a_2 & b_2 & c_2 \\ a_3 & b_3 & c_3 \end{bmatrix}} = \frac{k_1b_2c_3 + b_1c_2k_3 + c_1k_2b_3 - c_1b_2k_3 - k_1c_2b_3 - b_1k_2c_3}{a_1b_2c_3 + b_1c_2a_3 + c_1a_2b_3 - c_1b_2a_3 - a_1c_2b_3 - b_1a_2c_3} \quad (7\text{-}7)$$

$$y = \frac{\begin{bmatrix} a_1 & k_1 & c_1 \\ a_2 & k_2 & c_2 \\ a_3 & k_3 & c_3 \end{bmatrix}}{\begin{bmatrix} a_1 & b_1 & c_1 \\ a_2 & b_2 & c_2 \\ a_3 & b_3 & c_3 \end{bmatrix}} = \frac{a_1k_2c_3 + k_1c_2a_3 + c_1a_2k_3 - c_1k_2a_3 - a_1c_2k_3 - k_1a_2c_3}{a_1b_2c_3 + b_1c_2a_3 + c_1a_2b_3 - c_1b_2a_3 - a_1c_2b_3 - b_1a_2c_3} \quad (7\text{-}8)$$

$$z = \begin{bmatrix} a_1 & b_1 & k_1 \\ a_2 & b_2 & k_2 \\ a_3 & b_3 & k_3 \\ a_1 & b_1 & c_1 \\ a_2 & b_2 & c_2 \\ a_3 & b_3 & c_3 \end{bmatrix} = \frac{a_1b_2k_3 + b_1k_2a_3 + k_1a_2b_3 - k_1b_2a_3 - a_1k_2b_3 - b_1a_2k_3}{a_1b_2c_3 + b_1c_2a_3 + c_1a_2b_3 - c_1b_2a_3 - a_1c_2b_3 - b_1a_2c_3} \quad (7\text{-}9)$$

Example 7-100

Use Cramer's Rule to solve the following system of simultaneous equations:

$2x + 3y - 4z = 1$

$3x - y - 2z = 4$

$4x - 7y - 6z = -7$

SOLUTION

We will setup a coefficient matrix **A,** constant matrix **b** and variable matrix **X**.

$$A = \begin{bmatrix} 2 & 3 & -4 \\ 3 & -1 & -2 \\ 4 & -7 & -6 \end{bmatrix} \quad b = \begin{bmatrix} 1 \\ 4 \\ -7 \end{bmatrix} \quad X = \begin{bmatrix} x \\ y \\ z \end{bmatrix}$$

Whereas **AX** = **b** is the matrix equation.

We wish to find the determinant of matrix **A**.

$$\det(A) = \begin{vmatrix} 2 & 3 & -4 \\ 3 & -1 & -2 \\ 4 & -7 & -6 \end{vmatrix}$$

We will use the cofactor expansion method on matrix **A**. We will do a cofactor expansion on the first row in order to compute the determinant.

$$\det(\mathbf{A}) = 2 \begin{vmatrix} -1 & -2 \\ -7 & -6 \end{vmatrix} - 3 \begin{vmatrix} 3 & -2 \\ 4 & -6 \end{vmatrix} - 4 \begin{vmatrix} 3 & -1 \\ 4 & -7 \end{vmatrix} = 82$$

Remember to check for sign changes for the coefficients in the position matrix given in Figure 7-6. For instance, the a_{12} element is positive in the **A** matrix. However, this element has a negative sign in the position matrix of Figure 7-6. So we must use -3 instead of +3 when computing the determinant.

Note: We could find the determinant of A by using equation 7-2 which is the augmented method.

Likewise, we can use the cofactor expansion to find the determinants of the substitutional matrices.

Second, we build the $\mathbf{A_1}$ cofactor expansion matrix by removing the coefficients associated with x and replacing them with the constant matrix coefficients.

$$\mathbf{A_1} = \begin{bmatrix} 1 & 3 & -4 \\ 4 & -1 & -2 \\ -7 & -7 & -6 \end{bmatrix}$$

We wish to find the determinant of matrix $\mathbf{A_1}$.

$$\det(\mathbf{A_1}) = \begin{vmatrix} 1 & 3 & -4 \\ 4 & -1 & -2 \\ -7 & -7 & -6 \end{vmatrix}$$

We will use the cofactor expansion method on matrix $\mathbf{A_1}$. We will do a cofactor expansion on the third column in order to compute the determinant.

$$\det(\mathbf{A_1}) = -4 \begin{vmatrix} 4 & -1 \\ -7 & -7 \end{vmatrix} + 2 \begin{vmatrix} 1 & 3 \\ -7 & -7 \end{vmatrix} - 6 \begin{vmatrix} 1 & 3 \\ 4 & -1 \end{vmatrix} = 246$$

The coefficient a_{23} is negative in the $\mathbf{A_1}$ matrix. However, this element has a negative sign in the position matrix of Figure 7-6. So we must use +2 instead of -2 when computing the determinant.

Third, we build the $\mathbf{A_2}$ cofactor expansion matrix by removing the coefficients associated with y and replacing them with the constant matrix coefficients.

$$\mathbf{A_2} = \begin{bmatrix} 2 & 1 & -4 \\ 3 & 4 & -2 \\ 4 & -7 & -6 \end{bmatrix}$$

We wish to find the determinant of matrix $\mathbf{A_1}$.

$$\det(\mathbf{A_2}) = \begin{vmatrix} 2 & 1 & -4 \\ 3 & 4 & -2 \\ 4 & -7 & -6 \end{vmatrix}$$

We will use the cofactor expansion method on matrix $\mathbf{A_2}$. We will do a cofactor expansion on the third row in order to compute the determinant.

$$\det(\mathbf{A_2}) = 4 \begin{vmatrix} 1 & -4 \\ 4 & -2 \end{vmatrix} + 7 \begin{vmatrix} 2 & -4 \\ 3 & -2 \end{vmatrix} - 6 \begin{vmatrix} 2 & 1 \\ 3 & 4 \end{vmatrix} = 82$$

The coefficient a_{32} is negative in the $\mathbf{A_2}$ matrix. However, this element has a negative sign in the position matrix of Figure 7-6. So we must use +7 instead of -7 when computing the determinant.

Fourth, we build the $\mathbf{A_3}$ cofactor expansion matrix by removing the coefficients associated with z and replacing them with the constant matrix coefficients.

$$\mathbf{A_3} = \begin{bmatrix} 2 & 3 & 1 \\ 3 & -1 & 4 \\ 4 & -7 & -7 \end{bmatrix}$$

We wish to find the determinant of matrix $\mathbf{A_3}$.

$$\det(\mathbf{A_3}) = \begin{vmatrix} 2 & 3 & 1 \\ 3 & -1 & 4 \\ 4 & -7 & -7 \end{vmatrix}$$

We will use the cofactor expansion method on matrix $\mathbf{A_3}$. We will do a cofactor expansion on the second row in order to compute the determinant.

$$\det(\mathbf{A_3}) = -3 \begin{vmatrix} 3 & 1 \\ -7 & -7 \end{vmatrix} - 1 \begin{vmatrix} 2 & 1 \\ 4 & -7 \end{vmatrix} - 4 \begin{vmatrix} 2 & 3 \\ 4 & -7 \end{vmatrix} = 164$$

The coefficients a_{21} and a_{23} are positive in the $\mathbf{A_3}$ matrix. However, these elements have negative signs in the position matrix of Figure 7-6. So we must use -3 and -4 respectively instead of +3 and +4 when computing the determinant.

The values of x, y, and z that satisfy the linear equations are computed using the equations 7-7, 7-8, and 7-9.

$$x = \frac{246}{82} = 3$$

$$y = \frac{82}{82} = 1$$

$$z = \frac{164}{82} = 2$$

7.45 MATRIX ALGEBRA

Matrix algebra differs somewhat from standard algebra.

1. Equality: Two matrices, $\mathbf{A}$ and $\mathbf{B}$, are equal only if they have the same numbers of rows and columns and if all corresponding entries are equal.

2. Inequality: The $>$ and $<$ operators are not used in matrix algebra.

3. Commutative Law of Addition: $\mathbf{A} + \mathbf{B} = \mathbf{B} + \mathbf{A}$

4. Associative Law of Addition: $\mathbf{A} + (\mathbf{B+C}) = (\mathbf{A+B}) + \mathbf{C}$

5. Associative Law of Multiplication: $(\mathbf{AB})\mathbf{C} = \mathbf{A}(\mathbf{BC})$

6. Left Distributive Law: $\mathbf{A}(\mathbf{B+C}) = \mathbf{AB} + \mathbf{AC}$

7. Right Distributive Law: $(\mathbf{B+C})\mathbf{A} = \mathbf{BA} + \mathbf{CA}$

8. Scalar Multiplication: $k(\mathbf{AB}) = (k\mathbf{A})\mathbf{B} = \mathbf{A}(k\mathbf{B})$

It is important to recognize that matrix multiplication is not commutative.
That is, $\mathbf{AB} \neq \mathbf{BA}$

7.45.1 MATRIX ADDITION

Addition (subtraction) of two matrices is possible only if both matrices have the same shape and size (i.e., order). It is accomplished by adding (subtracting) the corresponding entries of the two matrices.

Example 7-101

Add the following matrices.

$$A = \begin{bmatrix} 3 & 1 & 2 \\ 0 & 6 & 0 \\ 1 & 2 & 5 \end{bmatrix} \qquad B = \begin{bmatrix} 0 & 1 & 2 \\ 0 & 5 & 7 \\ 9 & 3 & 6 \end{bmatrix}$$

SOLUTION

$$A + B = \begin{bmatrix} 3 & 2 & 4 \\ 0 & 11 & 7 \\ 10 & 5 & 11 \end{bmatrix}$$

7.45.2 MATRIX MULTIPLICATION

A matrix can be multiplied by another matrix, but only if the left-hand matrix has the same number of columns as the right-hand matrix has rows. *Matrix multiplication* occurs by multiplying the elements in each left-hand matrix row by the entries in each right-hand column, adding the products, and placing the sum at the intersection point of the participating row and column.

Matrix division can only be accomplished by multiplying by the inverse of the denominator. There is no specific division operation in matrix algebra.

Example 7-102

Determine the product matrix **C**:

$$C = \begin{bmatrix} 3 & 4 & 3 \\ 5 & 2 & 6 \end{bmatrix} \times \begin{bmatrix} 7 & 12 \\ 11 & 8 \\ 9 & 10 \end{bmatrix}$$

SOLUTION

The left-hand matrix has three columns, and the right-hand matrix has three rows. Therefore, the two matrices can be multiplied.

The new matrix **C** will have the following size:

$$\mathbf{C} = \begin{bmatrix} a_{11} & a_{12} \\ a_{21} & a_{22} \end{bmatrix}$$

The first row of the left-hand matrix and the first column of the right-hand matrix are worked with first. The corresponding entries are multiplied and the products are summed.

$$c_{11} = (1 \times 7) + (4 \times 11) + (3 \times 9) = 78$$

The intersection of the top row and left column [a_{11}] is the entry in the upper left-hand corner of the matrix C.

The first row of the left-hand matrix and the second column of the right-hand matrix are worked with second. The corresponding entries are multiplied and the products are summed.

$$c_{12} = (1 \times 12) + (4 \times 8) + (3 \times 10) = 74$$

The intersection of the top row and right column [a_{12}] is the entry in the upper right-hand corner of the matrix C.

The second row of the left-hand matrix and the first column of the right-hand matrix are worked with third. The corresponding entries are multiplied and the products are summed.

$$c_{21} = (5 \times 7) + (2 \times 11) + (6 \times 9) = 111$$

The intersection of the bottom row and left column [a_{21}] is the entry in the lower left-hand corner of the matrix C.

The second row of the left-hand matrix and the second column of the right-hand matrix are worked with fourth. The corresponding entries are multiplied and the products are summed.

$$c_{22} = (5 \times 12) + (2 \times 8) + (6 \times 10) = 136$$

The intersection of the bottom row and right column [a_{22}] is the entry in the lower right-hand corner of the matrix C.

The product matrix is $\mathbf{C} = \begin{bmatrix} 78 & 74 \\ 111 & 136 \end{bmatrix}$

Example 7-103

Find the product of the two matrices:

$$A = \begin{bmatrix} 1 & 0 & 2 \\ 3 & -1 & 6 \\ 0 & 2 & 3 \end{bmatrix} \qquad B = \begin{bmatrix} 2 & 0 \\ -1 & 2 \\ 0 & 5 \end{bmatrix}$$

SOLUTION

Let C = A × B. The new matrix size is 3 × 2.

$$\mathbf{C} = \begin{bmatrix} (1 \times 2) + (0 \times -1) + (2 \times 0) & (1 \times 0) + (0 \times 2) + (2 \times 5) \\ (3 \times 2) + (-1 \times -1) + (6 \times 0) & (3 \times 0) + (-1 \times 2) + (6 \times 5) \\ (0 \times 2) + (2 \times -1) + (3 \times 0) & (0 \times 0) + (2 \times 2) + (3 \times 5) \end{bmatrix}$$

$$\mathbf{C} = \begin{bmatrix} 2 & 10 \\ 7 & 28 \\ -2 & 19 \end{bmatrix}$$

7.45.3 TRANSPOSE

The *transpose*, A^t, of an m × n matrix A is an n × m matrix constructed by taking the *ith* row and making it the *ith* column. The diagonal is unchanged.

Example 7-104

Find the transpose of matrix **A**.

$$\mathbf{A} = \begin{bmatrix} 1 & 6 & 9 \\ 2 & 3 & 4 \\ 7 & 1 & 5 \end{bmatrix}$$

SOLUTION

$$\mathbf{A}^t = \begin{bmatrix} 1 & 2 & 7 \\ 6 & 3 & 1 \\ 9 & 4 & 5 \end{bmatrix}$$

The following equations are the characteristics of the transpose.

a) $(\mathbf{A}^t)^t = \mathbf{A}$ (7-10)

b) $(k\mathbf{A}^t)^t = k(\mathbf{A}^t)$ (7-11)

c) $\mathbf{I}^t = \mathbf{I}$ (7-12)

d) $(\mathbf{A} \times \mathbf{B})^t = \mathbf{B}^t \times \mathbf{A}^t$ (7-13)

e) $(\mathbf{A} + \mathbf{B})^t = \mathbf{A}^t + \mathbf{B}^t$ (7-14)

f) $|\mathbf{A}^t| = |\mathbf{A}|$ (7-15)

7.45.4 SINGULARITY AND RANK

A singular matrix is one whose determinant is zero. Similarly, a nonsingular matrix is one whose determinant is nonzero.

The rank of a matrix is the maximum number of linearly independent row or column vectors. A matrix has rank r if it has at least one nonsingular square sub-matrix of order r but has no nonsingular square sub-matrix of order more than r. While the sub-matrix must be square (in order to calculate the determinant), the original matrix need not be.

The rank of $m \times n$ matrix will be, at most, the smaller of m and n. The rank of a null matrix is zero. The ranks of a matrix and its transpose are the same. If a matrix is in echelon form, the rank will be equal to the number of rows containing at least one nonzero entry. For a 3×3 matrix, the rank can be either be 3 (if it is nonsingular), 2 (if any one of its 2×2 sub-matrices is nonsingular), 1 (if it and all 2×2 sub-matrices are singular), or 0 (if it is null).

The determination of rank is somewhat laborious if done by hand. Either the matrix is reduced to echelon form by using elementary row operations, or exhaustive enumeration is used to create the sub-matrices and many determinants are calculated. If a matrix has more rows than columns and row-reduction is used, the work required to put the matrix in echelon form can be reduced by working with the transpose of the original matrix.

Example 7-105

What is the rank of matrix **A**?

$$A = \begin{bmatrix} 1 & -1 & -1 \\ -3 & 3 & 0 \\ 2 & 2 & 4 \end{bmatrix}$$

SOLUTION

Matrix **A** is singular because the det (**A**) = 0. However, there is at least one 2 × 2 nonsingular sub-matrix:

$$\begin{vmatrix} 1 & -2 \\ -3 & 3 \end{vmatrix} = (1 \times 3) - (-3 \times 2) = -3$$

Therefore, the rank is 2.

Example 7-106

Determine the rank of matrix **A** by reducing it to echelon form.

$$A = \begin{bmatrix} 7 & 4 & 9 & 1 \\ 0 & 2 & -5 & 3 \\ 0 & 4 & -10 & 6 \end{bmatrix}$$

SOLUTION

By inspection, the matrix can be row-reduced by subtracting two times the second row from the third row. The matrix cannot be further reduced. Since there are two nonzero rows, the rank is 2.

$$\begin{bmatrix} 7 & 4 & 9 & 1 \\ 0 & 2 & -5 & 3 \\ 0 & 0 & 0 & 0 \end{bmatrix}$$

7.11.5 CLASSICAL ADJOINT

The classical adjoint is the transpose of the cofactor matrix. The resulting can be designated as A_{adj}, adj{**A**} or A^{adj}.

Example 7-107

What is the classical adjoint of matrix **A**?

$$\mathbf{A} = \begin{bmatrix} 2 & 3 & -4 \\ 0 & -4 & 2 \\ 1 & -1 & 5 \end{bmatrix}$$

SOLUTION

The matrix of cofactors is

$$\begin{bmatrix} -18 & 2 & 4 \\ -11 & 14 & 5 \\ -10 & -4 & -8 \end{bmatrix}$$

The transpose of the matrix of cofactors is

$$\mathbf{A}_{adj} = \begin{bmatrix} -18 & -11 & -10 \\ 2 & 14 & -4 \\ 4 & 5 & -8 \end{bmatrix}$$

7.45.6 INVERSE

The product of a matrix **A** and its inverse, $\mathbf{A}^{-1}$, is the identity matrix, **I**. Only square matrices have inverses, but not all square matrices are invertible. A matrix has an inverse if and only if it is nonsingular (i.e., its determinant is nonzero).

$$\mathbf{A} \times \mathbf{A}^{-1} = \mathbf{A}^{-1} \times \mathbf{A} = \mathbf{I}$$

$$(\mathbf{A} \times \mathbf{B})^{-1} = \mathbf{B}^{-1} \times \mathbf{A}^{-1}$$

The inverse of a 2 × 2 matrix is easily determined by formula.

$$A = \begin{bmatrix} a & b \\ c & d \end{bmatrix}$$

$$A^{-1} = \frac{\begin{bmatrix} d & -b \\ -c & a \end{bmatrix}}{|A|}$$

For a 3 × 3 or larger matrix, the inverse is determined by dividing every entry in the classical adjoint by the determinant of the original matrix. Equation 7-16 is used to compute the inverse of a 3 × 3 matrix.

$$A^{-1} = \frac{A_{adj}}{|A|} \qquad (7\text{-}16)$$

Example 7-108

What is the inverse of matrix **A**?

$$\mathbf{A} = \begin{bmatrix} 4 & 5 \\ 2 & 3 \end{bmatrix}$$

SOLUTION

$$|A| = (4 \times 3) - (2 \times 5) = 2$$

The inverse is

$$\mathbf{A}^{-1} = \frac{\begin{bmatrix} 3 & -5 \\ -2 & 4 \end{bmatrix}}{2} = \begin{bmatrix} 3/2 & -5/2 \\ -1 & 2 \end{bmatrix}$$

We can check the solution.

$$A \times A^{-1} = \begin{bmatrix} 4 & 5 \\ 2 & 3 \end{bmatrix} \times \begin{bmatrix} 3/2 & -5/2 \\ -1 & 2 \end{bmatrix} = \begin{bmatrix} 6-5 & -10+10 \\ 3-3 & -5+6 \end{bmatrix} = \begin{bmatrix} 1 & 0 \\ 0 & 1 \end{bmatrix} = I$$

7.45.7 EIGENVALUES AND EIGENVECTORS

Eigenvalues and eigenvectors (also known as a characteristic values and *characteristic vectors*) of a square matrix A are the scalars λ and matrices X such that both sides of equation 7-17 is satisfied.

$$A \times X = \lambda X \qquad (7\text{-}17)$$

The scalar λ is an eigenvalue of A if and only if the matrix $(\lambda I - A)$ is singular, that is, det($\lambda I - A$) = 0. This equation is called the characteristic equation of the matrix A. When expanded, the determinant is called the characteristic polynomial.

If all of the eigenvalues are unique (i.e., non-repeating), then equation 7-18 is valid:

$$[\lambda I - A] \times X = 0 \qquad (7\text{-}18)$$

Example 7-109

Find the eigenvalues and nonzero eigenvectors of the matrix A.

$$A = \begin{bmatrix} 2 & 4 \\ 6 & 4 \end{bmatrix}$$

SOLUTION

$$\lambda I - A = \begin{bmatrix} \lambda & 0 \\ 0 & \lambda \end{bmatrix} - \begin{bmatrix} 2 & 4 \\ 6 & 4 \end{bmatrix} = \begin{bmatrix} \lambda-2 & -4 \\ -6 & \lambda-4 \end{bmatrix}$$

The characteristic polynomial is found by setting the determinant {det ($\lambda I - A$)} equal to zero.

$$(\lambda - 2) \times (\lambda - 4) - (-6) \times (-4) = 0$$

$$\lambda^2 - 6\lambda - 16 = (\lambda - 8) \times (\lambda + 2) = 0$$

The roots of the characteristic polynomial are $\lambda = +8$ and $\lambda = -2$. These are the eigenvalues of A.

Substituting $\lambda = 8$,

$$\lambda \mathbf{I} - \mathbf{A} = \begin{bmatrix} 8-2 & -4 \\ -6 & 8-4 \end{bmatrix} = \begin{bmatrix} 6 & -4 \\ -6 & 4 \end{bmatrix}$$

This can be interpreted as the linear equation $6x_1 - 4x_2 = 0$. The values of x that satisfy this equation define the eigenvector. An eigenvector $\mathbf{X}$ associated with the eigenvalue $+8$ is

$$\mathbf{X} = \begin{bmatrix} x_1 \\ x_2 \end{bmatrix} = \begin{bmatrix} 4 \\ 6 \end{bmatrix}$$

All other eigenvectors for this eigenvalue are multiples of $\mathbf{X}$. Normally $\mathbf{X}$ is reduced to smallest integers.

$$\mathbf{X} = \begin{bmatrix} 2 \\ 3 \end{bmatrix}$$

Similarly, the eigenvector associated with the eigenvalue -2 $(\lambda = 2)$ is

$$\mathbf{X} = \begin{bmatrix} x_1 \\ x_2 \end{bmatrix} = \begin{bmatrix} +4 \\ -4 \end{bmatrix} \quad \text{Reducing this to smallest integers yields } \mathbf{X} = \begin{bmatrix} +1 \\ -1 \end{bmatrix}.$$

7.46 MATLAB

MATLAB is short for "MATrix LABoratory." It is a numerical computing environment and programming language. MATLAB was invented in the late 1970s by Cleve Moler. MATLAB allows matrix manipulation, plotting of functions and data, implementations of algorithms, creation of user interfaces, and interfacing with programs in other languages. MATLAB code is written in C programming language.

MATLAB commands are sometimes terminated with a semicolon (;) and sometimes not. The difference is that the result of a calculation is printed to the screen when there is no semicolon but no printing is done when there is a semicolon.

7.46.1 VECTORS AND MATRICES IN MATLAB

A vector refers to a one dimensional ($1 \times N$ or $N \times 1$) matrix, commonly referred to as an array in other programming languages.

A matrix generally refers to a multi-dimensional matrix, that is, a matrix with more dimension for instance an $N \times M$, an $N \times M \times L$, etc., where N, M, and L are greater than 1.

7.46.2 DEFINING AN ARRAY IN MATLAB

The syntax for defining an array is *init:increment:terminator*
init is the starting value. *increment* is step-size or the amount MATLAB will add to the init value or previous count. *terminator* is the final value.

Example 7-110

Use MATLAB to display an array C with the following size 1:2:9

SOLUTION

>> is the symbol for prompt or cursor in MATLAB. We will the letter C as a variable.

At the prompt we type: >> C = 1:2:9

Press enter on the keyboard.

MATLAB will display

C =
     1   3   5   7

Example 7-111

Use MATLAB to display an array D with the following size 1:3:9

SOLUTION

We will the letter D as a variable.

At the prompt we type: >> D = 1:3:9

Press enter on the keyboard.

MATLAB will display

 D =
     1   4   7

Note: You can use the up-arrow key (↑) to scroll through previous commands in MATLAB.

The increment value can actually be left out of the syntax for an array. MATLAB will use a default value of 1.

Example 7-112

Use MATLAB to display an array E with the following size 1:5.

SOLUTION

We will the letter E as a variable.

At the prompt we type: >> E = 1:5

Press enter on the keyboard.

MATLAB will display

 E =
    1   2   3   4   5

7.46.3 BUILDING A MATRIX IN MATLAB

MATLAB treats all its variables as though they were matrices. Important subclasses of matrices include row vectors (matrices with a single row and possibly several columns) and column vectors (matrices with a single column and possibly several rows). In MATLAB you don't have to declare the size of your variable. MATLAB decides how big the variable is when you try to put a value in it. The easiest way to define a row vector is to list its values inside of square brackets, and separated by spaces or commas. The easiest way to define a column vector is to list its values inside of square brackets, separated by semicolons or line breaks.

Example 7-113

Use MATLAB to build the following 2×2 matrix $A = \begin{bmatrix} 1 & -3 \\ 3 & 2 \end{bmatrix}$

SOLUTION

At the prompt we type: $>> A = [1, -3; 3, 2]$

Press <u>enter</u> on the keyboard.

MATLAB will display

A =

    1 -3
    3   2

Example 7-114

Use MATLAB to build the following 2×1 matrix $D = \begin{bmatrix} 4 \\ -1 \end{bmatrix}$

SOLUTION

At the prompt we type: $>> D = [4; -1]$

Press <u>enter</u> on the keyboard.

MATLAB will display

D =

     4
   -3

Example 7-115

Use MATLAB to build the following 1×3 matrix $G = \begin{bmatrix} 6, 0 - 7 \end{bmatrix}$

SOLUTION

At the prompt we type: $>> G = [6, 0, -7]$

Press <u>enter</u> on the keyboard.

MATLAB will display

G =

   6 0 -7

7.46.4 ELEMENTARY OPERATIONS ON MATRICES

Table 7-7 shows how MATLAB performs addition, subtraction, multiplication, division, and exponentiation on matrices.

In order to add or subtract matrices, they must be of the same matrix size. In order to perform Array Multiplication, Array Right Division, and Array Left Division the two matrices must be of the same size. In order to perform Matrix Multiplication on two matrices, the number of columns in the first matrix must equal the number of rows in the second matrix. Matrix Multiplication is performed in Example 7-117.

TABLE 7-7

Element-by-Element Operation	Representative Data $A = [a_1 \ a_2 \ ... \ a_n]$, $B = [b_1 \ b_2 \ ... \ b_n]$, $c = $ <a scalar>
Scalar Addition	$A + c = [a_1 + c \quad a_2 + c \ ... \ a_n + c]$
Scalar Subtraction	$A - c = [a_1 - c \quad a_2 - c \ ... \ a_n - c]$
Scalar Multiplication	$A *c = [a_1 *c \quad a_2 *c \ ... \ a_n *c]$
Scalar Division	$A/c = c\backslash A = [a_1 /c \quad a_2 /c \ ... \ a_n /c]$
Array Addition	$A + B = [a_1 + b_1 \quad a_2 + b_2 \ ... \ a_n + b_n]$
Array Subtraction	$A - B = [a_1 - b_1 \quad a_2 - b_2 \ ... \ a_n - b_n]$
Array Multiplication	$A./*B = [a_1*b_1 \quad a_2*b_2 \ ... \ a_n*b_n]$
Array Right Division	$A./B = [a_1/b_1 \quad a_2 /b_2 \ ... \ a_n /b_n]$
Array Left Division	$B.\backslash A = [a_1/b_1 \quad a_2 /b_2 \ ... \ a_n /b_n]$
Array Exponentiation	$A .^c = [a_1 {}^c \quad a_2 {}^c \ ... \ a_n {}^c]$ $c .^A = [c {}^{a_1} \quad c {}^{a_2} \ ... \ c^{a_n}]$ $A .^B = [a_1 {}^{b_1} \quad a_2 {}^{b_2} \ ... \ a_n {}^{bn}]$

Example 7-116

Use MATLAB to add the following matrices $A = \begin{bmatrix} 1 & -3 \\ 3 & 2 \end{bmatrix}$ and $E = \begin{bmatrix} 4 & -2 \\ 0 & 9 \end{bmatrix}$.

SOLUTION

At the prompt we type: >> A = [1, -3; 3, 2]
Press <u>enter</u> on the keyboard.

MATLAB will display

A =
      1 -3
      3   2

At the prompt we type: >> A = [4, -2; 0, 9]
Press <u>enter</u> on the keyboard.

MATLAB will display

A =
      4 -2
      0   9

At the prompt we type: >> F = A + E

Press <u>enter</u> on the keyboard.

MATLAB will display

F =
      5 -5
      3   11

Example 7-117

Use the matrices of Example 7-33 to perform the following operation in MATLAB: $Y = A - E$.

SOLUTION

At the prompt we type: >> Y = A - E

Press <u>enter</u> on the keyboard.

MATLAB will display

Y =

$$\begin{array}{cc} -3 & -1 \\ 3 & -7 \end{array}$$

Example 7-118

Use MATLAB to perform the Matrix Multiplication of D × T where

$$D = \begin{bmatrix} 4 \\ -1 \end{bmatrix} \quad \text{and} \quad T = \begin{bmatrix} 8 & 3 \end{bmatrix}.$$

SOLUTION

At the prompt we type: >> D = [4; -1]

Press <u>enter</u> on the keyboard.

MATLAB will display

D =

    4

   -3

At the prompt we type: >> T = [8 3]

Press <u>enter</u> on the keyboard.

MATLAB will display

T =

   8 3

At the prompt we type: >> P = D*T

Press <u>enter</u> on the keyboard.

P =

   32 12

   -8 -7

7.46.5 USING MATLAB TO FIND THE DETERMINANT

det (X) is the determinant of the square matrix (X).

Example 7-119

Use MATLAB to find the determinant of the following matrix below.

$$A = \begin{bmatrix} 4 & -6 \\ 2 & 3 \end{bmatrix}$$

SOLUTION

At the prompt we type: >> A = [4,-6;2,3];

Press enter on the keyboard.

At the prompt we type: >> det (A)

MATLAB will display

ans =
   24

Example 7-120

Use MATLAB to find the determinant of the following matrix below.

$$A = \begin{bmatrix} 1 & 1 & -3 \\ 4 & 0 & 2 \\ -1 & 1 & 2 \end{bmatrix}$$

SOLUTION

At the prompt we type: >> A = [1, 1, -3; 4, 0, 2; -1, 1, 2];

Press enter on the keyboard.

At the prompt we type: >> det (A)

MATLAB will display

ans =
        -24

7.46.6 USING MATLAB TO FIND THE INVERSE

inv(X) is the inverse of the square matrix (X). A warning message is printed if (X) is badly scaled or nearly singular.

Example 7-121

Use MATLAB to find the determinant of the following matrix below.

$$A = \begin{bmatrix} 3 & 5 & 7 \\ -1 & 6 & 11 \\ 9 & -10 & 4 \end{bmatrix}$$

SOLUTION

At the prompt we type: >> A = [3, 5, 7; -1, 6, 11; 9, -10, 4];

Press enter on the keyboard.

At the prompt we type: >> inv (A)

MATLAB will display

ans =
        0.2200   -0.1478   0.0213
        0.1691   -0.0837   -0.0657
       -0.0722   0.1232   0.0378

7.46.7 USING MATLAB TO FIND THE TRANSPOSE

B = transpose of (A) is called for the syntax A when A is an object.

Example 7-122

Use MATLAB to find the transpose of the following matrix below.

$$A = \begin{bmatrix} 0 & 1 \end{bmatrix}$$

SOLUTION

At the prompt we type: >> A = [0 1];

Press <u>enter</u> on the keyboard.

At the prompt we type: >>B = transpose (A)

MATLAB will display

B =

      0
      1

Example 7-123

Use MATLAB to find the transpose of the following matrix below.

$$A = \begin{bmatrix} 1 & -2 & 3 \\ 0 & 1 & 15 \end{bmatrix}$$

SOLUTION

At the prompt we type: >> A = [1, -2, 3;0, 1, 15];

Press <u>enter</u> on the keyboard.

At the prompt we type: >>B = transpose (A)

MATLAB will display

B =

    1   0
  -2   1
   3 15

Example 7-124

Use MATLAB to find the transpose of the following matrix below.

$$R = \begin{bmatrix} 2 & 4 & 1 \\ 3 & -1 & 0 \\ 0 & 5 & -6 \end{bmatrix}$$

SOLUTION

At the prompt we type: >> R = [1, 4, 1; 3, -1, 0; 0, 5, -6];

Press <u>enter</u> on the keyboard.

At the prompt we type: >>C = transpose (R)

MATLAB will display

C =

```
    2   3   0
    4  -1   5
    1   0   6
```


7.46.8 USING MATLAB TO FIND THE RANK OF A MATRIX

Rank (A) provides an estimate of the number of linearly independent rows or columns of a matrix A.

Example 7-125

Use MATLAB to find the rank of this matrix.

$$A = \begin{bmatrix} 2 & 4 \\ 8 & 16 \end{bmatrix}$$

SOLUTION

At the prompt we type: >> A = [2,4;8,16];

Press <u>enter</u> on the keyboard.

At the prompt we type: >> rank (A)

MATLAB will display

ans =
      1

Example 7-126

Use MATLAB to find the rank of this matrix.

$$A = \begin{bmatrix} 0 & 1 & -3 & 4 \\ 2 & -2 & -8 & -7 \\ -3 & 6 & 6 & 4 \end{bmatrix}$$

SOLUTION

At the prompt we type: >> A = [0,1,-3,4;2,-2,-8,-7;-3,6,6,4];

Press <u>enter</u> on the keyboard.

At the prompt we type: >> rank (A)

MATLAB will display

ans =
      3

7.46.9 USING MATLAB TO SOLVE SIMULTANEOUS EQUATIONS

When using MATLAB to solve simultaneous equations it is necessary to invert the Coefficient Matrix. A^{-1} denotes inverse in MATLAB. In order to inverse a matrix it must have the same number of rows as columns.

Example 7-127

Use MATLAB to find the solution set (i_1, i_2) of the following set of simultaneous equations.

$$6i_1 - 4i_2 = -12 \quad 1)$$

$$-13i_1 + 2i_2 = 20 \quad 2)$$

SOLUTION

The Coefficient Matrix, Variable Matrix and the Constant Matrix are shown below.

$$A = \begin{bmatrix} 6 & -4 \\ -13 & 2 \end{bmatrix} \quad i = \begin{bmatrix} i_1 \\ i_2 \end{bmatrix} \quad b = \begin{bmatrix} -12 \\ 20 \end{bmatrix}$$

The simultaneous equations are written in Matrix Form below:

$A \times i = b$

$i = A^{-1} \times b$

At the prompt we type: >> A = [6, -4; -13, 2]
Press <u>enter</u> on the keyboard.

MATLAB will display

A =

     6   -4
   -13   2

At the prompt we type: >> b = [-12; 20]

Press <u>enter</u> on the keyboard.

MATLAB will display

b =

   -12
    20

At the prompt we type: >> U = inv(A)

Press <u>enter</u> on the keyboard.

MATLAB will display

```
U =
        -0.05   -0.1
        -0.325  -0.15
```

At the prompt we type: >> i = U*b

Press <u>enter</u> on the keyboard.

MATLAB will display

```
i =
        -1.4
         0.9
```

7.46.10 SOLVING FOR EIGENVALUES AND EIGENVECTORS USING MATLAB

E = eig(X)

E is a vector containing the eigenvalues of a square matrix X.
[V,D] = eig(X)

The function [**V,D**] produces a diagonal matrix D of eigenvalues and a full matrix V whose columns are the corresponding eigenvectors so that X * V = V *D.
D and V are N × N matrices.

[V,D] = eig(X,'nobalance')

The function [V,D] performs the computation with balancing disabled, which sometimes give more accurate results for certain problems with unusual scaling.

E = eig(A,B)

This function creates a vector containing the generalized eigenvalues of square matrices A and B.

[V,D] = eig(A,B)

The function [V,D] produces a diagonal matrix D of eigenvalues and a full matrix V whose columns are the corresponding eigenvectors so that A * V = B *V*D.

Example 7-128

Use MATLAB to find the eigenvalues of the following matrix.

$$A = \begin{bmatrix} 2 & 5 \\ 1 & 8 \end{bmatrix}$$

SOLUTION

At the prompt we type: >> A = [2, 5; 1, 8]
Press <u>enter</u> on the keyboard.

MATLAB will display

A =
    2   5
    1   8

At the prompt we type: >> E = eig(A)

Press <u>enter</u> on the keyboard.

MATLAB will display

E =
    1.2583
    8.7417

The eigenvalues are $\lambda_1 = 1.2583$ and $\lambda_2 = 8.7417$.

Example 7-129

Use MATLAB to find the eigenvalues and eigenvectors of **A**?

$$\mathbf{A} = \begin{bmatrix} 8 & 4 \\ 6 & 4 \end{bmatrix}$$

SOLUTION

At the prompt we type: >> A = [8, 4; 6, 4]
Press <u>enter</u> on the keyboard.

MATLAB will display

A =

       8   4
       6   4

At the prompt we type: >> [V,D] = eig(A)

Press <u>enter</u> on the keyboard.

MATLAB will display

V =

  0.7722 -0.4810
  0.6354   0.8767

D =

  11.2915   0
     0   0.7085

The eigenvalues are $\lambda_1 = 11.2915$ and $\lambda_2 = 0.7085$.

For $\lambda_1 = 11.2915$, the eigenvector is

$$X = \begin{bmatrix} 0.7722 \\ 0.6354 \end{bmatrix}$$

For $\lambda_2 = 0.7085$, the eigenvector is

$$X = \begin{bmatrix} -0.4810 \\ 0.8767 \end{bmatrix}$$

Example 7-130

Use MATLAB to find the eigenvalues and eigenvectors of matrices **A** and **B**?

$$A = \begin{bmatrix} 14 & -4 & 8 \\ -4 & 4 & -3 \\ 8 & -3 & 6 \end{bmatrix} \quad B = \begin{bmatrix} 10 & 5 & 6 \\ 5 & 10 & 6 \\ 6 & 6 & 10 \end{bmatrix}$$

SOLUTION

At the prompt we type: >> A = [14, -4, 8; -4, 4, -3; 8, -3, 6]
Press <u>enter</u> on the keyboard.

MATLAB will display

A =

```
        14  -4  8
        -4   4 -3
         8  -3  6
```

At the prompt we type: >> B = [10, 5, 6; 5, 10, 6; 6, 6, 10]
Press <u>enter</u> on the keyboard.

MATLAB will display

B =

```
        10   5  6
         5  10  6
         6   6 10
```

At the prompt we type: >> [V,D] = eig(A,B)

Press enter on the keyboard.

MATLAB will display

V =

0.5890	0.6166	-0.2430
-0.7190	0.3856	0.5773
0.3690	-0.6863	0.7795

D =

3.1213	0	0
0	0.4023	0
0	0	0.1021

The eigenvalues are $\lambda_1 = 3.1213$, $\lambda_2 = 0.4023$, and $\lambda_3 = 0.1021$.

For $\lambda_1 = 3.1213$, the eigenvector is

$$X = \begin{bmatrix} 0.5890 \\ -0.7190 \\ 0.3690 \end{bmatrix}$$

For $\lambda_2 = 0.4023$, the eigenvector is

$$X = \begin{bmatrix} 0.6166 \\ 0.3856 \\ -0.6863 \end{bmatrix}$$

For $\lambda_3 = 0.1021$, the eigenvector is

$$X = \begin{bmatrix} -0.2430 \\ 0.5773 \\ 0.7795 \end{bmatrix}$$

Example 7-131

Use MATLAB to find the eigenvalues and eigenvectors of matrices **A** and **B**?

$$A = \begin{bmatrix} 2 & -3 \\ 1 & 5 \end{bmatrix} \quad B = \begin{bmatrix} 8 & 5 \\ 4 & 4 \end{bmatrix}$$

SOLUTION

At the prompt we type: >> A = [2, -3; 1, 5]]
Press <u>enter</u> on the keyboard.

MATLAB will display

A =

         2 -3
         1 5

At the prompt we type: >> B = [8,5; 4,4]
Press <u>enter</u> on the keyboard.

MATLAB will display

B =

         8 5
         4 4

At the prompt we type: >> [V,D] = eig(A,B)

Press <u>enter</u> on the keyboard.

MATLAB will display

V =

    1.0000   -0.6026
         0   0.7980

D =

    0.2500   0
         0   4.3333

The eigenvalues are $\lambda_1 = 0.25$, and $\lambda_2 = 0.4023$.

For $\lambda_1 = 0.25$, the eigenvector is

$$X = \begin{bmatrix} 1 \\ 0 \end{bmatrix}$$

For $\lambda_2 = 4.333$, the eigenvector is

$$X = \begin{bmatrix} -0.6026 \\ 0.7980 \end{bmatrix}$$

Measurement Systems

CHAPTER 8
MEASUREMENT SYSTEMS

8.1 THE U.S. CUSTOMARY SYSTEM OF MEASUREMENT

8.1.1 LENGTH

There are four basic units in the U.S. customary system used to measure length. They are the inch, the foot, the yard, and the mile. Table 8-1 gives the relationships among these measurements of length.

TABLE 8-1

U.S. Customary Units of Length or Distance

12 inches (in.) = 1 foot (ft)	36 inches = 1 yard (yd)
3 feet (ft) = 1 yard (yd)	5,280 feet (ft) = 1 mile (mi)

The width of a U.S. quarter is a good estimate of an *inch*, as shown in Figure 8-1. Lengths measured in inches include the sizes of men's trousers, belts, shirts, and jackets. The diagonal distance in inches from the corner to opposite corner of a television screen determines its size, such as 19 in. or 36 in. television screens. Photographs and picture frames, such as (5 ×7) or (8 ×10) are measured in inches.

FIGURE 8-1

A *foot* is 12 inches, or about the width of placemats for a dining table as shown in Figure 8-2. We use feet to measure lengths varying in size by increments of 12 inches. Lumber is sold by the linear foot. Human heights are also often measured in feet (and inches), for example, 5 ft 7 in, 6 ft 5 in, or 5 ft 1 in. Elevation, such as the height of mountains and altitude of airplanes, is designated in feet.

FIGURE 8-2

A mile is 5,280 feet, or the length of approximately eight city blocks. The Romans originally used the mile. They considered a mile to be 1,000 paces of 5 feet each. Distances between cities and the lengths travel on a road, street, or highway are measured in miles.

The yard is 3 feet or 36 inches. Yards are sometimes used instead of feet. For example yards are used to measure fabric, carpet, and U.S. football fields.

8.1.2 WEIGHT AND MASS

The terms weight and mass are commonly used interchangeably. In technical, engineering, and scientific applications, the *mass* of an object is the quantity of material that makes up the object. The *weight* is a measure of the earth's gravitational pull on the object. Three commonly used measuring units for weight or mass in the U.S. customary system is the ounce, pound, and ton. Table 5-2 gives the relationships among these three measures of weight or mass.

TABLE 8-2

U.S. Customary Units of Weight or Mass
16 ounces (oz) = 1pound (lb)
2,000 pounds (lb) = 1 ton (T)

The ounce is $\frac{1}{16}$ of a pound. Ounces are used to measure light weight items like first-class letters or small packages, tubes of toothpaste or medicinal ointments, canned goods, and dry-packaged foods like pasta, candy, and gravy mixes.

A pound is equal to 16 ounces. The term is derived from an old English word for weight. Many small, medium, and large items of merchandise are measured in pounds, like grocery and market items, people's weights, and air pressure in automotive tires. The pound is also used to calculate shipping charges for merchandise and parcel post packages.

A ton is 2,000 pounds. The word originally meant a weight or measure. The ton is used for extremely heavy items, such as very large volumes of grain, the weights of huge animals like elephants and the weights by which coal and iron are sold.

8.1.3 CAPACITY AND VOLUME

The U.S. customary units of measure for capacity or volume are the ounce, cup, pint, quart, and gallon. Table 8-3 gives the relationships among the liquid measures for capacity or volume.

TABLE 8-3

U.S. Customary Units of Liquid Capacity or Volume

3 teaspoons (t) = 1 tablespoon (T)	2 tablespoons (T) = 1 ounce (oz)
8 ounces (oz) = 1 cup (c)	4 cups (c) = 1 quart (qt)
2 cups (c) = 1 pint (pt)	4 quarts (qt) = 1 gallon (gal)
2 pints (pt) = 1 quart (qt)	

In the U.S. customary system the term ounce represents both weight and liquid capacity. The measures are different and have no common relationship. The context of the problem will suggest whether the unit for weight or capacity is meant. A liquid ounce is a volume, not a weight. Liquid ounces are used for bottled medicine, canned or bottled carbonated beverages, baby bottles and formula, and similar-sized quantities. Bottles of perfume are typically measured in ounces, as shown in Figure 8-3.

FIGURE 8-3

124

A cup is equal to 8 ounces. The term is derived from an old English word for tub, a kind of container. This measure is about the volume of a coffee cup, as shown in Figure 8-4. Cups are most often used for 8 oz quantities in cooking. Measuring cups used for cooking usually divide their contents into cups and portions of cups.

FIGURE 8-4

A pint is two cups. Its name comes from an old English word meaning the spot that marks a certain level in a measuring device. Automobile motor additives, ice cream, and produce like strawberries are packaged in pint containers.

A quart is two pints, or four cups, or 32 ounces. The term is derived from an Old English word for fourth. It is a fourth of a gallon. Mayonnaise, mustard and various citrus juices are often sold in quart containers. Quarts are used to measure liquid quantities in cooking and also the capacities of cookware like mixing bowls, pots, and casserole dishes.

A gallon is four quarts. It is based on the "wine gallon" of British origin. Milk is sold by the gallon, ½ gallon, quart and pint as shown in Figure 8-5. Motor fuel, heating oil and paint are usually sold by the gallon, as are large quantities of liquid propane and various chemicals. Often, statistics on liquid consumption, such as water or alcoholic beverages, are reported in gallons consumed per individual during a specified time period.

FIGURE 5-5

8.2 CONVERSIONS BETWEEN U.S. CUSTOMARY UNITS OF MEASUREMENT

Using the relationship between two units of measure, we can form a ratio in two different ways that has a value of 1. We call this type of ratio a *unity ratio*. Since a ratio is a fraction, a unity ratio is a fraction with one unit of measure in the numerator but an equivalent and different unit of measure in the denominator. Some examples of unity ratios are $\dfrac{36 \text{ in.}}{1 \text{ yd.}}$, $\dfrac{16 \text{ oz}}{1 \text{ lb.}}$, and $\dfrac{2,000 \text{ lb}}{1 \text{ ton.}}$.

Steps to do when converting from one U.S. customary unit of measure to another using unity ratios:

1. Set up the original amount as a fraction with the original unit of measure in the numerator.

2. Multiply this fraction by a unity ratio with the original unit in the denominator and the new unit in the numerator.

3. Reduce like units of measure and all numbers wherever possible.

Example 8-1

Convert 60 quarts (qt) to gallons (gal).

SOLUTION

$$\frac{60 \text{ qts}}{1} \times \frac{1 \text{ gal}}{4 \text{ qts}} = 15 \text{ gal}$$

Example 8-2

How many yards are in 500 inches?

SOLUTION

$$\frac{500 \text{ in.}}{1} \times \frac{1 \text{ yd}}{36 \text{ in.}} = 13.89 \text{ yd}$$

Example 8-3

Suppose that the center of a pro football team weighs 320 pounds (lb). What is his weight in ounces (oz)?

SOLUTION

$$\frac{320 \text{ lb}}{1} \times \frac{16 \text{ oz}}{1 \text{ lb}} = 5120 \text{ oz}$$

Example 5-4

How ounces (oz) exist in 0.005 tons (T)?

SOLUTION

$$\frac{0.005 \text{ T}}{1} \times \frac{2000 \text{ lb}}{1 \text{ T}} \times \frac{16 \text{ oz}}{1 \text{ lb}} = 160 \text{ oz}$$

8.3 INTRODUCTION TO THE METRIC SYSTEM

While the English system is based on one standard, the Metric system is subdivided into two interrelated standards: the **MKS** and the **CGS**. **MKS** stands for Meter-Kilogram-Second. **CGS** stands for Centimeter-Gram-Second. Thus, the MKS system uses Meters, Kilograms, and Seconds. Furthermore, the CGS system uses Centimeters, Grams, and Seconds.

The *metric system* is an international system of measurement that uses standard units and powers-of-ten prefixes to indicate other units of measure. The *meter* is used for length or distance, the *gram* is used for weight, and the *liter* is used for capacity or volume. A prefix is affixed to the standard unit to indicate a measure greater than the standard unit or less than the standard unit. All metric units of length, weight, and volume are expressed either as a standard unit or as a standard unit with a prefix. Table 8-4 shows the metric prefixes and their relationship to the standard unit.

TABLE 8-4

Metric Prefixes

Prefix	Power of 10 Value
exa (E)	10^{18}
peta (P)	10^{15}
tera (T)	10^{12}
giga (G)	10^{9}
mega (M)	10^{6}
kilo (k)	10^{3}
hecto (h)	10^{2}
deka (da)	10^{1}
Standard Unit	10^{0} or 1
deci (d)	10^{-1}
centi (c)	10^{-2}
milli (m)	10^{-3}
micro (μ)	10^{-6}
nano (n)	10^{-9}
pico (p)	10^{-12}
femto (f)	10^{-15}
atto (a)	10^{-18}

5.3.1 LENGTH

The *meter* is the standard unit for measuring length. Both *meter* and *metre* are acceptable spellings for this unit of measure. A meter is about 39.37 in., or 3.37 in. (approximately $3\frac{1}{2}$ in.) longer than a yard, as shown in Figure 8-6.

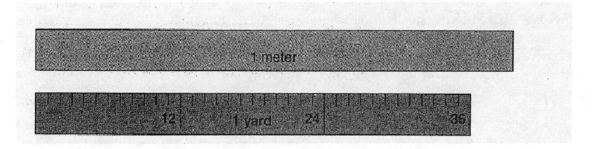

FIGURE 8-6

We use the meter to measure lengths and distances like room dimensions, land dimensions, lengths of poles, heights of mountains, and heights of buildings, as shown in Figure 8-7. The abbreviation for meter is m.

FIGURE 8-7

A *kilometer* is 1,000 meters and is used for longer distances. The abbreviation for kilometer is km. The prefix kilo means 1,000. We measure the distance from the city to another, one country to another, or one landmark to another in kilometers. One kilometer is about five city blocks. One mile is about eight city blocks. An average walking speed is 1 km in about 10 min.

To measure objects less than 1 m long, we commonly use the centimeter (cm). The prefix *centi* means "$\frac{1}{100}$ of" and a centimeter is one-hundredth of a meter. A *centimeter* is about the width of a thumbtack head, somewhat less than $\frac{1}{2}$ in. We use centimeters to measure medium-sized objects such as tires, clothing, textbooks, and television pictures, as shown in Figure 8-8.

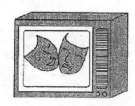

FIGURE 8-8

Many objects are too small to be measured in centimeters, so we use a millimeter (mm), which is "$\frac{1}{1000}$ of" a meter. It is about the thickness of a plastic credit card or a dime. Certain film sizes, bolt and nut sizes, the length of insects, and other such items are measured in millimeters.

129

8.3.2 WEIGHT

The standard unit for measuring mass in the metric system is the *gram*. A *gram* is the mass of 1 cubic centimeter (cm³) of water at its maximum density. The metric unit for measuring weight is the Newton (N); however, in common usage the gram is used in comparing metric and U.S. customary units of weight. A cubic centimeter is a cube whose edges are each 1 centimeter long. It is a little smaller than a sugar cube. The abbreviation *g* is used for *gram*. We use grams to measure small or light objects such as paper clips, cubes of sugar, coins, and bars of soap.

A *kilogram* (kg) is 1,000 grams. Since a cube 10 cm on each edge will be 1,000 cm³, the weight of water required to fill this cube is 1,000 grams or 1 kilogram. A kilogram is approximately 2.2 lb. The kilogram is used to measure the weight of people, meat, automobiles, etc.

The gram is used to measure small objects, and the milligram $\left(\frac{1}{1,000} \text{ of a gram}\right)$ is used to measure *very* small objects. Milligrams are too small for ordinary uses; however, pharmacists and manufacturers use milligrams (mg) to measure small amounts of drugs, vitamins, and medications.

8.3.3 CAPACITY AND VOLUME

A *liter* (L) is the volume of a cube 10 cm on each edge. It is a standard metric unit of capacity. Like the meter, it may be spelled *liter* or *litre*, but we use the spelling *liter*. A cube 10 cm on each edge filled with water weighs approximately 1 kg, so 1 L of water weighs about 1 kg. One liter is just a little larger than a liquid quart. Soft drinks are sold in 2-liter bottles as shown in Figure 8-9. Some service stations sell gasoline by the liter.

1 liter — about the volume of a quart of milk or a soft drink in a plastic bottle

FIGURE 8-9

A liter is 1,000 cm^3, so $\dfrac{1}{1,000}$ of a liter, or a *millimeter*, has the same volume as a cubic centimeter, as shown in Figure 8-10. Most liquid medicine is labeled and sold in milliliters (mL) or cubic centimeters (cc or cm^3). Medicines, perfumes, and other very small quantities are measured in milliliters.

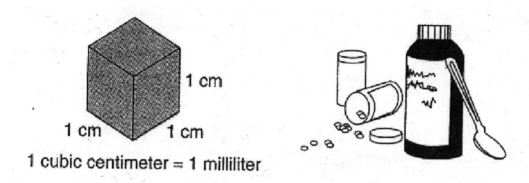

1 cubic centimeter = 1 milliliter

FIGURE 8-10

Example 8-5

Convert 1175 grams (g) of sulfur to kilograms (kg).

SOLUTION

$$\frac{1175\,\text{g}}{1} \times \frac{1\,\text{kg}}{10^3\,\text{g}} = 1.175\,\text{kg}$$

Example 8-6

How many milliliters (mL) are in 4.85×10^{-4} liters (L)?

SOLUTION

$$\frac{4.85 \times 10^{-4}\,\text{L}}{1} \times \frac{10^3\,\text{mL}}{1\,\text{L}} = 0.485\,\text{mL}$$

Example 8-7

If the length between two people is 590 hecto-meters (hm), what is this length in kilo-meters (km)?

SOLUTION

$$\frac{590\,\text{hm}}{1} \times \frac{10^2\,\text{m}}{1\,\text{hm}} \times \frac{1\,\text{km}}{10^3\,\text{m}} = 59\,\text{km}$$

Example 8-8

Suppose that an ant migrated 12,475 pico-meters (pm), what is his distance in micro-meters (μm)?

SOLUTION

$$\frac{12,475\,\text{pm}}{1} \times \frac{10^{-12}\,\text{m}}{1\,\text{pm}} \times \frac{1\,\mu\text{m}}{10^{-6}\,\text{m}} = 0.0125\,\mu\text{m}$$

Example 8-9

How many liters are in 100,000 cm^3?

SOLUTION

$$\frac{100,000\,\text{cm}^3}{1} \times \frac{1\,\text{mL}}{1\,\text{cm}^3} \times \frac{10^{-3}\,\text{L}}{1\,\text{mL}} = 100\,\text{L}$$

Example 8-10

If a mass of clay weighs 0.0019 kg, then what is its weight in deci-grams (dg)?

SOLUTION

$$\frac{0.0019\,\text{kg}}{1} \times \frac{10^3\,\text{g}}{1\,\text{kg}} \times \frac{1\,\text{dg}}{10^{-1}\,\text{g}} = 19\,\text{dg}$$

8.4 CONVERSIONS BETWEEN U.S. CUSTOMARY MEASURES AND METRIC MEASURES

Converting a measure from the U.S. customary system to the metric system, and vice versa, is often necessary because both systems are used in the United States. Also, a company that uses the U.S. customary system in the United States often needs to convert to the metric system to market its product in other countries. Table 8-5 is a list of conversion factors. More comprehensive conversion tables are given in the appendix of this book. In regard to Table 8-5, dry quarts are less common than liquid quarts. If the type of quart (dry or liquid) is not specified then use liquid quarts.

TABLE 8-5
Conversion Factors

1 in = 2.540 cm
1 cm = 0.3937 in.
1 ft = 0.3048 m
1 yd = 0.914 m
1 m = 1.09 yd
1 mi = 1.609 km
1 m = 39.97 in.
1 m = 3.281 ft.
1 km = 0.6215 mi
$1 \text{ in}^2 = 6.452 \text{ cm}^2$
$1 \text{ m}^2 = 10.76 \text{ ft}^2$
1 kg = 2.2046 lb
1 g = 0.0353 oz
1 L = 0.91 dry qt (dry measure)
1 L = 1.06 liquid qt (liquid measure)
$1 \text{ L} = 1 \times 10^{-3} \text{ m}^3$
$1 \text{ mL} = 1 \text{ cm}^3$

$1 m^2 = 10000 cm^2$ $1 ft^2 = 144 in^2$

Example 8-11

Convert 65 mph to ft/s.

SOLUTION

$$\frac{65 \text{ mi.}}{h} \times \frac{5280 \text{ ft}}{1 \text{ mi}} \times \frac{1 \text{ h}}{3600 \text{ s}} = 95.33 \frac{\text{ft}}{\text{s}}$$

Example 8-12

How many ounces are in a 355 mL of Pepsi soft drink?

SOLUTION

$$\frac{355 \text{ mL}}{1} \times \frac{10^{-3} \text{ L}}{1 \text{ mL}} \times \frac{1.06 \text{ qt}}{1 \text{ L}} \times \frac{2 \text{ pt}}{1 \text{ qt}} \times \frac{16 \text{ oz}}{1 \text{ pt}} = 12 \text{ oz}$$

Example 8-13

Suppose that a football player can bench press 350 lb. What is this weight in kg?

SOLUTION

$$\frac{350\,\text{lb}}{1} \times \frac{1\,\text{kg}}{2.2\,\text{lb}} = 159\,\text{kg}$$

Example 8-14

If the distance between two towns is 131 miles, what is this distance in kilo-meters (km)?

SOLUTION

$$\frac{131\,\text{mi.}}{1} \times \frac{1.609\,\text{km}}{1\,\text{mi.}} = 210.78\,\text{km}$$

Example 8-15

How many cubic feet (ft^3) are in a volume of 40,000 mm^3 of water?

SOLUTION

$$\frac{40{,}000\,\text{mm}^3}{1} \times \left(\frac{1\,\text{m}}{10^3\,\text{mm}}\right)^3 \times \left(\frac{1\,\text{ft}}{0.3048\,\text{m}}\right)^3 = 0.0124\,\text{ft}^3$$

Example 8-16

How many ounces (oz) are contained in 125 cm^3?

SOLUTION

$$\frac{125\,\text{cm}^3}{1} \times \frac{0.033814\,\text{oz}}{1\,\text{cm}^3} = 4.227\,\text{oz}$$

Example 8-17

Convert $\dfrac{1}{16}$ oz of magnesium to grams (g).

SOLUTION

$$\frac{1}{16} = 6.25 \times 10^{-2}$$

$$\frac{6.25 \times 10^{-2} \text{ oz}}{1} \times \frac{1 \text{ g}}{0.035274 \text{ oz}} = 1.772 \text{ g}$$

8.5 TEMPERATURE FORMULAS

In this section we will use the Celsius, Fahrenheit, Rankine and Kelvin temperature scales for computations. We will convert Celsius to Fahrenheit and vice versa. We will convert Celsius to Kelvin and vice versa. We will convert Fahrenheit to Rankine and vice versa.

8.5.1 CELSIUS/KELVIN TEMPERATURE CONVERSIONS

The *Kelvin* scale is one scale used to measure temperature in the metric system of measurement. Units on the scale are abbreviated with a capital K (without the symbol ° because these units are called *kelvins*) and are measured from the absolute zero, the temperature at which all heat is said to be removed from matter. Another metric temperature scale is the *Celsius* scale (abbreviated °C), which has as its zero the freezing point of water. The Kelvin and Celsius scales are related such that absolute zero on the Kelvin scale is the same as -273°C on the Celsius. Each unit of change on the Kelvin scale is equal to 1 degree of change on the Celsius scale; that is, the size of a Kelvin and a Celsius degree is the same on both scales. Equation 8-1 shows the temperature conversion from the Celsius scale to the Kelvin scale.

$$K = °C + 273 \qquad (8\text{-}1)$$

Example 8-18

Convert 25°C on the Celsius scale to the Kelvin scale?

SOLUTION

Using equation 5-1 and solving for K yields:

K = °C + 273 = 25 + 273 = 298 K

Example 8-19

Convert 400 K on the Kelvin scale to the Celsius scale?

SOLUTION

Using equation 5-1 and solving for °C gives us:

°C = K – 273 = 400 – 273 = 127°C

8.5.2 RANKINE/FAHRENHEIT TEMPERATURE CONVERSIONS

The U.S. customary temperature scale that starts at absolute zero is called the *Rankine* scale. It is related to the more familiar *Fahrenheit* scale, which places the freezing point of water at 32°. One degree of change on the Rankine scale equals 1 degree of change on the Fahrenheit scale. Absolute zero (the zero for the Rankine scale) corresponds to 460 degrees below zero (-460°) on the Fahrenheit scale. Equation 8-2 shows the temperature conversion from the Fahrenheit scale to the Rankine scale.

°R = °F + 460   (8-2)

Example 8-20

Convert the temperature 15°F on the Fahrenheit scale to the Rankine scale.

SOLUTION

Using equation 5-2 and solving for °R will give us:

°R = °F + 460 = 15 + 460 = 475°R

Example 8-21

Convert the temperature 542°R on the Rankine scale to the Fahrenheit scale.

SOLUTION

Using equation 5-2 and solving for °F yields:

$$°F = °R - 460 = 542 - 460 = 82°F$$

8.5.3 CONVERT FAHRENHEIT TO CELSIUS TEMPERATURES AND CELSIUS TO FAHRENHEIT TEMPERATURES

The Celsius and Fahrenheit scales are the most common temperature scales used for reporting air and body temperatures. The formulas for converting temperatures using these two scales are more complicated than the previous ones because 1 degree of change on the Celsius scale does not equal 1 degree of change on the Fahrenheit scale. Equations 8-3 and 8-4 show the temperature conversions from the Fahrenheit scale to the Celsius scale and the Celsius scale to the Fahrenheit scale, respectively.

$$°C = \frac{5}{9}(°F - 32) \qquad (8-3)$$

$$°F = (\frac{5}{9}°C) + 32 \qquad (8-4)$$

Example 8-22

Change 212° F (the boiling point of water) to degrees Celsius.

SOLUTION

Using equation 5-3 and solving for °C yields:

$$°C = \frac{5}{9}(°F - 32) = \frac{5}{9}(212 - 32) = \frac{5}{9}(180) = 100°C$$

Example 8-23

Convert 0°C (the freezing point of water) to degrees Fahrenheit.

SOLUTION

Using equation 5-4 and solving for °F yields:

$$°F = (\frac{5}{9}°C) + 32 = (\frac{5}{9} \times 0) + 32 = 0 + 32 = 32°F$$

8.6 USAGE OF THE CIRCLE

A circle is sketched in Figure 8-11. The center, circumference, diameter, radius, and semicircle of a circle are shown in that figure.

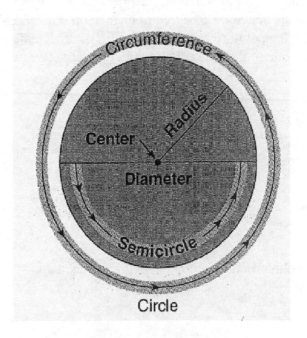

Circle

FIGURE 8-11

A *circle* is a closed curved line with points that lie in a plane and are the same distance from the *center* of the figure. The *center* of a circle is the point that is the same distance from every point on the circumference of the circle. The *radius* is a straight-line segment from the center of a circle to a point on the circle. It is half the diameter. The *diameter* of a circle is a straight-line segment from a point on the circle through the center to another point on the circle. The *circumference* of a circle is the perimeter or length of the closed curved line that forms the circle. A *semicircle* is half a circle and is created by drawing a diameter.

The circle is a geometric form with a special relationship between its circumference and its diameter. If we divide the circumference of any circle by its diameter, the quotient is always the same number. Equation 8-5 shows the calculation for π. Equation 8-6 is used to compute the circumference of a circle. Equation 8-7 is used to compute the diameter of a circle.

$$\pi = \frac{\text{Circumference}}{\text{Diameter}} = \frac{C}{d} = 3.1415927 \qquad (8\text{-}5)$$

$$C = \pi \times d \text{ or } C = 2\pi \times r \qquad (8\text{-}6)$$

$$d = 2 \times r \text{ or } r = \frac{1}{2} \times d \qquad (8\text{-}7)$$

If we divide a circle into two semicircles and then subdivide each semicircle into pie-shaped pieces, we will get the shape shown in Figure 8-12(a). If we spread the upper and lower pieces together, we get the results in Figure 8-12(b). Now if we push the upper and lower pieces together, the result approximates the rectangle in Figure 8-12(c), whose length is one-half the circumference and whose width is the radius. The area of a circle is the length multiplied by the width. Equation 8-8 is used for calculating the area of a circle.

$$A = \frac{1}{2}(2\pi r)(r) = \pi r^2 \qquad (8\text{-}8)$$

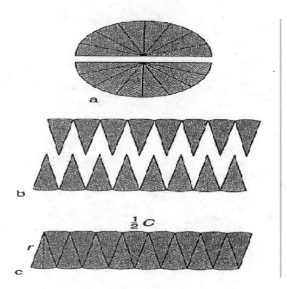

FIGURE 8-12

Since most conductors are circular, as shown in Figure 8-13, we may determine the cross-sectional area from either the radius or the diameter. Equation 8-9 computes the area of a circle using the diameter.

$$A = \pi r^2 = \pi \left(\frac{d}{2}\right)^2 = \frac{\pi d^2}{4} \qquad (8\text{-}9)$$

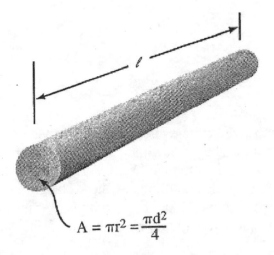

$$A = \pi r^2 = \frac{\pi d^2}{4}$$

FIGURE 8-13

Example 8-24

Find the area of a circle whose radius is 16.8 m.

SOLUTION

Using equation 8-8,

$$A = \pi r^2 = \pi (16.8 \text{ m})^2 = \pi (282.24) = 886.68 \text{ m}^2$$

Example 8-25

A 15 inch diameter wheel has a 3 inch hole in the center. Find the area of a side of the wheel.

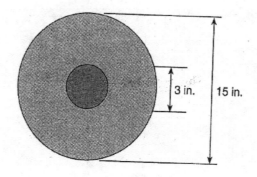

SOLUTION

Outside Radius: $r = \dfrac{15}{2} = 7.5$ in.

Inside Radius: $r = \dfrac{3}{2} = 1.5$ in.

$A_{outside} = \pi\, r^2 = \pi\, (7.5)^2 = \pi\, (56.25) = 176.71458$ in^2

$A_{inside} = \pi\, r^2 = \pi\, (1.5)^2 = \pi\, (2.25) = 7.06858$ in^2

Area of wheel (ring) [A_{wheel}] = $A_{outside}$ - A_{inside}

$A_{wheel} = 176.71458 - 7.06858 = 169.6$ in^2

The American Wire Gauge system for specifying wire diameters was developed using a unit called the circular mil (CM), which is defined as the area contained within a circle having a diameter of 1 mil (1 mil = 0.001 inch). Furthermore, 1000 mils = 1 in. A circular mil is shown in Figure 8-14(a). A square mil is defined as the area contained in a square having side dimensions of 1 mil. A square mil is shown in Figure 8-14(b). Figure 8-15 shows that the area of a circular mil is smaller than the area of a square mil. Because not all conductors have circular cross-sections, it is occasionally necessary to convert areas expressed in square mils into circular mils.

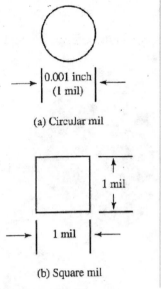

(a) Circular mil

(b) Square mil

FIGURE 8-14

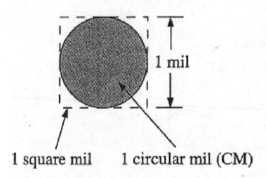

1 square mil   1 circular mil (CM)

FIGURE 8-15

Suppose that a wire has the circular cross section shown in Figure 8-14(a). The area in square mils of a circular cross section is expressed by equation 8-10:

$$A = \pi r^2 = \frac{\pi d^2}{4} = \frac{\pi (1\,\text{mil})^2}{4} = \frac{\pi}{4}\,\text{sq. mil} \qquad (8\text{-}10)$$

The equation above implies that:

$$1\,\text{CM} = \frac{\pi}{4}\,\text{sq mils}$$

$$1\,\text{sq mil} = \frac{4}{\pi}\,\text{CM} = 1.273\,\text{CM}$$

For a wire with a diameter of N mils, equation 8-8 or equation 8-9 can be formed into equation 8-11. N can be any positive number.

$$A = \pi r^2 = \frac{\pi d^2}{4} = \frac{\pi N^2}{4} \text{ sq mils} \qquad (8\text{-}11)$$

Substituting the fact that $\frac{4}{\pi}$ CM = 1 sq mil, we have equation 8-12.

$$A = \frac{\pi N^2}{4} \text{ (sq mils)} = \left(\frac{\pi N^2}{4}\right) \times \left(\frac{4}{\pi} \text{ CM}\right) = N^2 \text{ CM} \qquad (8\text{-}12)$$

Since d = N, the area in circular mils is simply equal to the diameter in mils square. Equation 8-13 is used for calculating the area in circular mils.

$$A_{CM} = (d_{mils})^2 \qquad (8\text{-}13)$$

Verification that an area can simply be the diameter squared is provided in part by Figure 8-16 for diameters of 2 and 3 mils. Although some areas are not circular, they have the same area as 1 circular mil.

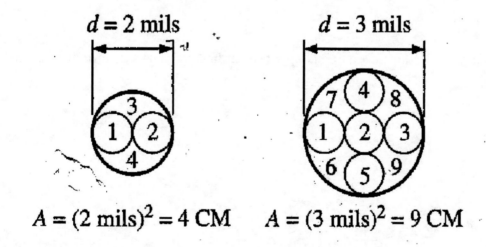

$$d = 2 \text{ mils} \qquad\qquad d = 3 \text{ mils}$$

$$A = (2 \text{ mils})^2 = 4 \text{ CM} \qquad A = (3 \text{ mils})^2 = 9 \text{ CM}$$

FIGURE 8-16

143

Example 8-26

Determine the cross-sectional area in circular mils of a wire having the following diameters:
a) 0.0159 inch
b) 0.500 inch

SOLUTION

a)

$$d = 0.0159 \text{ inch} \times 1000 \text{ mils/inch} = 15.9 \text{ mils}$$

Using equation 8-13,

$$A_{CM} = (15.9)^2 = 253 \text{ CM}$$

b)

$$d = 0.500 \text{ inch} \times 1000 \text{ mils/inch} = 500 \text{ mils}$$

Again using equation 8-13,

$$A_{CM} = (500)^2 = 250,000 \text{ CM}$$

Example 8-27

Determine the cross-sectional area of a copper bus bar having cross-sectional dimensions of 0.250 inch × 6.00 inch:

a) in square mils.
b) in circular mils.

SOLUTION

$$0.250 \text{ in.} \times \frac{1000 \text{ mils}}{1 \text{ in.}} = 250 \text{ mils}$$

$$6.00 \text{ in.} \times \frac{1000 \text{ mils}}{1 \text{ in.}} = 6000 \text{ mils}$$

a)

$$A_{sq\ mil} = (250 \text{ mils}) \times (6000 \text{ mils}) = 1,500,000 \text{ sq. mils}$$

144

b) $A_{CM} = 1,500,000$ sq. mils $\times \dfrac{4}{\pi}$ CM/sq. mil $= 1,910,000$ CM $= 1910$ MCM

8.7 TIME

1. The relationship among various units of time is given in Table 8-6 below.

TABLE 8-6

Units of Time

1 year (yr) = 12 months	1 minute = 60 seconds
1 year (yr) = 365 days (da)	1 millisecond (ms) = $\dfrac{1}{1,000}$ second
1 week (wk) = 7 days (da)	1 nanosecond (ns) = $\dfrac{1}{1,000,000,000}$ second
1 day (da) = 24 hours (hr)	1 minute (min) = 60 seconds (sec)
1 hour (hr) = 60 minutes (min)	1 hour (hr) = 3600 seconds (sec)

2. We can use either unity ratio or conversion factors to convert from one unit of time to another.

3. Suppose we have a 2 hr meeting and five items to be covered on our agenda. If we are to devote the same amount of time to each item, then each item will receive:

$$2 \text{ hr} \div 5 = \frac{2}{5} \text{ hr}$$

$$\frac{2}{5} \text{ hr} \times \left(\frac{60 \text{ min}}{1 \text{ hr}} \right) = 24 \text{ min}$$

Example 8-28

How many seconds are in 9 weeks?

SOLUTION

$$\frac{9 \text{ weeks}}{1} \times \frac{7 \text{ da}}{1 \text{ wk}} \times \frac{24 \text{ hr}}{1 \text{ da}} \times \frac{3600 \text{ sec}}{1 \text{ hr}} = 5.443 \times 10^6 \text{ sec}$$

4. Equate Time of Day Among Time Zones

   a. As our business operations becomes more global we have to account for the different *time zones* around the planet Earth. Earth is divided into time zones based on 1 day (24 hours) as shown in Figure 8-17.

FIGURE 8-17

   b. The imaginary horizontal line we call the equator divides Earth into two halves called *hemispheres.* Additional imaginary horizontal circles or rings are called *parallels of*

146

latitude. Since the equator is our north/south reference, we define it as 0° on the scale. The North Pole is at 90° N, and the South Pole is at 90°S.

c. We can relate this scale to the rectangular coordinate system and the vertical axis. Northern latitudes correspond to positive *y*-values on the rectangular coordinate system. Southern latitudes correspond to the negative *y*-values.

d. Imaginary circles drawn around the globe that pass through both the North and South Poles are called *meridians of longitude*. Figure 8-18 shows the equator, parallels, and meridians. Unlike the parallels, meridians are farthest apart at the equator and closest together at the North and South Poles. They roughly define the time zones.

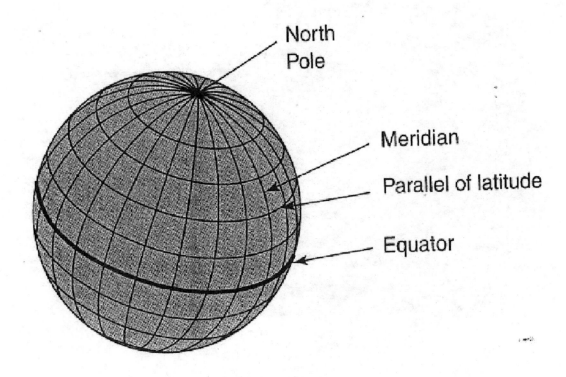

FIGURE 8-18

e. One complete rotation is 360°, so one time zone covers approximately 15° of Earth's rotation (360° ÷ 24 = 15°). We say approximately because time zone boundaries are not defined strictly by meridians. Actual time zone boundaries are defined by country, state, or province boundaries that are near a particular meridian. A few countries or small islands that are close to halfway between time zone boundaries define their time as a one-half difference from a neighboring time zone. To be sure how a country defines it time, consult an atlas or other reference.

f. Just as the equator is the longest parallel and is the zero line that separates north and south measures, one meridian must serve as zero for the east and west measures. All meridians are the same length, so one was arbitrarily selected; it is the one that passes through Greenwich England, and is called the *prime meridian*.

g. As the prime meridian (Figure 8-19) passes through the North and South Poles and becomes the 180° meridian to the side of Earth opposite Greenwich, England, it is called the *international date line*. In references that show appropriate time zone for a location (city, state, or country), the time is given as plus or minus a specified number of hours from *Greenwich Mean Time* (GMT).

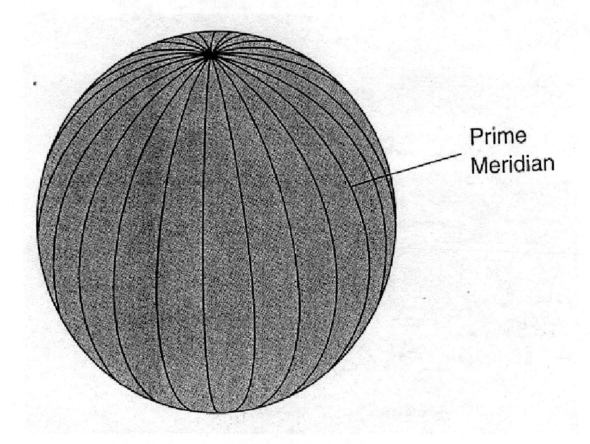

FIGURE 8-19

5.8 TIME ZONE

1. GMT	Military	Phonetic	Civilian Time Zone
+0:00	z	Zulu	GMT—Greenwich Mean
			UT or UTC—Universal (Coordinated)
			WET—Western European

Cities/Country
a. London, England
b. Dublin, Ireland
c. Edinburgh, Scotland
a. Lisbon, Portugal
b. Reykjavik, Iceland
c. Casablanca, Morocco

2. GMT	Military	Phonetic	Civilian Time Zone
-1:00	a	Alpha	WAT—West Africa

Cities/Country
a.   Azores, Cape Verde Islands

3. GMT	Military	Phonetic	Civilian Time Zone
-2:00	b	Bravo	AT--Azores

Cities/Country

4. GMT	Military	Phonetic	Civilian Time Zone
-3:00	c	Charlie	

Cities/Country
a. Brasilia, Brazil
b. Buenos Aires, Argentina
c. Georgetown, Guyana
d. Rio de Janeiro, Brazil

5. GMT	Military	Phonetic	Civilian Time Zone
-4:00	d	Delta	AST—Atlantic Standard

Cities/Country
a. Caracas, Venezuela
a. La Paz, Bolivia
b. Georgetown, Guyana

6. GMT	Military	Phonetic	Civilian Time Zone
-5:00	e	Echo	EST—Eastern Standard

Cities/Country
a. Atlanta, Georgia, USA

b. Bogota, Colombia
c. Boston, MA, USA
d. Lima, Peru
e. New York, NY, USA
f. Toronto, Canada

7. GMT	Military	Phonetic	Civilian Time Zone
-6:00	f	Foxtrot	CST—Central Standard

Cities/Country
a. Chicago, IL, USA
b. Dallas, TX, USA
c. Memphis, TN, USA
d. Mexico City, Mexico
e. New Orleans, LA, USA
f. Saskatchewan, Canada

8. GMT	Military	Phonetic	Civilian Time Zone
-7:00	g	Golf	MST—Mountain Standard

Cities/Country
a. Denver, CO, USA

9. GMT	Military	Phonetic	Civilian Time Zone
-8:00	h	Hotel	PST—Pacific Standard

Cities/Country
a. Los Angeles, CA, USA

10. GMT	Military	Phonetic	Civilian Time Zone
-9:00	j	Juliet	YST—Yukon Standard

Cities/Country
a. Whitehorse, Yukon, Canada
b. Juneau, Alaska, USA

11. GMT	Military	Phonetic
-10:00	k	Kilo

Civilian Time Zone	Cities/Country
AHST—Alaska-Hawaii Standard	Honolulu, Hawaii, USA
CAT—Central Alaska	Anchorage, Alaska, USA
HST—Hawaii Standard	Fairbanks, Alaska, USA
EAST—East Australian Standard	

12. GMT   Military   Phonetic   Civilian Time Zone
   -11:00   l   Lima   NT—Nome

Cities/Country
a.   Nome, Alaska, USA
b.   American Samoa
c.   Aleutian Islands

13. GMT   Military   Phonetic   Civilian Time Zone
   -12:00   m   Mike   IDLW—International Date Line West

Cities/Country
a.   Attu, Alaska, USA

14. GMT   Military   Phonetic
   +12:00   y   Yankee

Civilian Time Zone	Cities/Country
IDLE—International Date Line East	Wellington, New Zealand
NZST—New Zealand Standard	Fiji
NZT—New Zealand	Marshall Islands

15. GMT   Military   Phonetic   Civilian Time Zone
   +11:00   x   X-ray   Russia Zone 10

Cities/Country
a.   Tasmania
b.   Sydney, Australia; Micronesia

16. GMT   Military   Phonetic
   +10:00   w   Whiskey

Civilian Time Zone	Cities/Country
GST—Guam Standard, Russia	Tamuning, Guam
Zone 9	Vladivostok
	Papua, New Guinea

17. GMT   Military   Phonetic
   +9:00   v   Victor

Civilian Time Zone	Cities/Country

JST—Japan Standard, Russia   Korea, Singapore, Saipan
Zone 8   Tokyo, Malaysia

18. GMT   Military   Phonetic   Civilian Time Zone
    +8:00   u   Uniform   CCT—China Coast, Russia Zone 7

    Cities/Country
    a. Mongolia;
    b. Perth, Australia
    c. Beijing, China

19. GMT   Military   Phonetic
    +7:00   t   Tango

    Civilian Time Zone   Cities/Country
    WAST—West Australian Standard   Christmas Island
    Russia Zone 6   Australia, Java, Indonesia
                                    Vietnam, Laos

20. GMT   Military   Phonetic
    +6:00   s   Sierra

    Civilian Time Zone   Cities/Country
    ZP6—Chesapeake Bay, Russia   Omsk, Kazakhstan (East)
    Zone 5   Kyrgyzstan

21. GMT   Military   Phonetic
    +5:00   r   Romeo

    Civilian Time Zone   Cities/Country
    ZP5—Chesapeake Bay, Russia   Perm, Pakistan, Kazakhstan
    Zone 4   (West)

22. GMT   Military   Phonetic   Civilian Time Zone
    +4:00   q   Quebec   ZP4—Russian Zone 3

    Cities/Country
    a. Mauritius/Abu Dhabi, UAE
    b. Muscat, Aman
    c. Tblisi, Republic of Georgia
    d. Volgograd, Russia
    e. Kabul, Afghanistan

23. GMT   Military   Phonetic   Civilian Time Zone
    +3:00   p   Papa   BT—Baghdad, Russia Zone 2

   Cities/Country
   a. Kuwait
   b. Nairobi, Kenya
   c. Riyadh, Saudi Arabia
   d. Moscow, Russia
   e. Tehran, Iran

24. GMT   Military   Phonetic   Civilian Time Zone
    +2:00   o   Oscar   EET—Eastern European, Russia Zone 1

   Cities/Country
   a. Athens, Greece
   b. Helsinki, Finland
   c. Istanbul, Turkey
   d. Jerusalem, Israel
   e. Botswana, Zambia
   f. Mozambique
   g. Harare, Zimbabwe
   h. Egypt
   i. Johannesburg, South Africa
   j. Cape Town, South Africa

25. GMT   Military   Phonetic
    +1:00   n   November

   Civilian Time Zone   Cities/Country
   CET—Central European   Paris, France
   FWT—French Winter   Berlin, Germany
   MET—Middle European   Amsterdam
   MEWT—Middle European Winter   Netherlands
   SWT—Swedish Winter   Brussels, Belgium
                                              Vienna, Austria
                                              Madrid, Spain
                                              Rome, Italy
                                              Bern, Switzerland
                                              Stockholm, Sweden
                                              Oslo, Norway
                                              Nigeria

26. To determine the time in a different time zone:

i) Identify the GMT for both locations.
ii) Subtract the GMT for the location with the known time from the GMT for the location with the unknown time.
iii) Adjust the known time by the number of hours found in Step 2.

Example 8-29

Determine the time in Anchorage, Alaska, USA when it is 3:00 P.M. in Caracas, Venezuela.

SOLUTION

Anchorage: -10 GMT (Identify each GMT. Unknown time)
Caracas: -4 GMT (Known time of 3:00 P.M.)

-10 - (-4) = -6 (Interpret as 6 hours earlier.)
3:00 P.M. = 15:00 {Time on a 24-hr clock. (P.M. = time + 12 hr)}

15:00 – 6:00 = **9:00 A.M.**

Example 8-30

Students in Boston, Massachusetts, Ogden, Utah, and Honolulu, Hawaii, are arranging an interactive chat on the Internet. Is there a time that this can be arranged between 8:00 A.M. and 3:00 P.M. at each site? At what time would each student need to schedule the session according to the local time?

SOLUTION

Boston is –5 GMT; Ogden, Utah is –7 GMT; and Honolulu, Hawaii, is –10 GMT.

-10 – (-5) = - 10 + 5 = -5

Honolulu is 5 hours earlier than Boston. When it is 3:00 P.M., in Boston, it is 10 A.M. in Honolulu. When it is 1:00 P.M. in Boston, it is 8 A.M. in Honolulu. The chat could be arranged between 1:00 P.M. and 3:00 P.M. by Boston's time, which would be 8:00 A.M. to 10:00 A.M. Honolulu's time.

Since Ogden, Utah is between the time zones, the session would be between 8:00 A.M. and 3:00 P.M. for students at Ogden.

-7 – (-5) = -7 + 2 = -2

Ogden is 2 hours earlier than Boston, so the students in Ogden should schedule the chat between 11:00 A.M. and 1:00 P.M.

8.9 TIME ZONES IN NORTH AMERICA

1. Table 8-7 lists the North American time zone acronyms/abbreviations.

TABLE 8-7

Abbreviation	Full Name	Time Zone
NST	Newfoundland Standard Time	UTC – 3:30 hours
NDT	Newfoundland Daylight Time	UTC – 2:30 hours
AST	Atlantic Standard Time	UTC – 4 hours
ADT	Atlantic Daylight Time	UTC – 3 hours
EST	Eastern Standard Time	UTC – 5 hours
EDT	Eastern Daylight Time	UTC – 4 hours
CST	Central Standard Time	UTC – 6 hours
CDT	Central Daylight Time	UTC – 5 hours
MST	Mountain Standard Time	UTC – 7 hours
MDT	Mountain Daylight Time	UTC – 6 hours
PST	Pacific Standard Time	UTC – 8 hours
PDT	Pacific Daylight Time	UTC – 7 hours
AKST	Alaska Standard Time	UTC – 9 hours
AKDT	Alaska Daylight Time	UTC – 8 hours
HAST	Hawaii-Aleutian Standard Time	UTC – 10 hours
HADT	Hawaii-Aleutian Daylight Time	UTC – 9 hours

2. NST is 3 hours and 30 minutes behind Coordinated Universal Time (UTC). During the summer, daylight saving time (summer time) is observed and NDT is used instead. An email sent from someone in the NST time zone will have the time zone listed as "-0330" in the header. NST is used during winter in the Canadian province of Newfoundland and Labrador, except most of Labrador (the mainland part).

3. NDT is 2 hours and 30 minutes behind Coordinated Time (UTC). NDT is a daylight saving time (summer time) zone. It is generally only used during the summer. An email sent from someone in the NDT time zone will have the time zone listed as "-0230" in the header. NST is used during summer in the Canadian province of Newfoundland and Labrador, except most of Labrador (the mainland part).

4. AST is 4 hours behind Coordinated Universal Time (UTC). During the summer, daylight saving time (summer time) is observed and ADT is used instead. An email sent from someone in the AST time zone will have the time zone listed as "-0400" in the header. AST is used during winter in the following Canadian provinces (ADT during summer):

   a. Most of the mainland (Labrador) part of the province of Newfoundland and Labrador

   b. New Brunswick

   c. Nova Scotia

   d. Prince Edward Island

5. ADT is 3 hours behind Coordinated Universal Time (UTC). ADT is a daylight saving time (summer time) zone. It is generally only used during the summer. An email sent from someone in the ADT time zone will have the time zone listed as "-0300" in the header. ADT is used during summer in the following Canadian provinces (AST during winter):

   a. Most of the mainland (Labrador) part of the province of Newfoundland and Labrador

   b. New Brunswick

   c. Nova Scotia

   d. Prince Edward Island

6. EST is 5 hours behind Coordinated Universal Time (UTC). An email sent from someone in the EST time zone will have the time zone listed as "-0500" in the header. EST is used during winter in these places (EDT during summer):

   a.   Connecticut

b. Delaware
c. District of Columbia
d. Florida - Southern/Eastern parts

   except Bay, Calhoun, Escambia, Holmes, Jackson, Okaloosa, Santa Rosa, Walton and Washington counties and northern Gulf county - look in CST/CDT

e. Georgia
f. Indiana - all except for these north-western counties near Chicago

   Lake, Porter, La Porte, Newton, Jasper, Starke

   and these south-western counties in Indiana near Evansville

   Knox, Daviess, Gibson, Pike, Dubois, Posey, Vanderburgh, Warrick, Perry

g. Kentucky - eastern parts

   counties of Anderson, Bath, Bell, Boone, Bourbon, Boyd, Boyle, Bracken, Breathitt, Bullitt, Campbell, Carroll, Carter, Casey, Clark, Clay, Elliott, Estill, Fayette, Fleming, Floyd, Franklin, Gallatin, Garrard, Grant, Greenup, Hancock, Hansock, Hardin, Harlan, Harrison, Henry, Jackson, Jefferson, Jessamine, Johnson, Kenton, Knott, Knox, Larue, Laurel, Lawrence, Lee, Leslie, Letcher, Lewis, Lincoln, Madison, Magoffin, Marion, Martin, Mason, McCreary, Meade, Menifee, Mercer, Montgomery, Morgan, Nelson, Nicholas, Oldham, Owen, Owsley, Pendleton, Perry, Pike, Powell, Pulaski, Robertson, Rockcastle, Rowan, Scott, Shelby, Spencer, Taylor, Trimble, Washington, Wayne, Whitley, Wolfe, Woodford

h. Maine
i. Maryland
j. Massachusetts
k. Michigan - most except these western counties

   Dickinson, Gogebic, Iron, and Menominee - which are on CST/CDT

l. New Hampshire
m. New Jersey
n. New York
o. North Carolina
p. Ohio
q. Pennsylvania
r. Rhode Island
s. South Carolina
t. Tennessee - eastern counties

Anderson, Blount, Bradley, Campbell, Carter, Claiborne, Cocke, Grainger, Greene, Hamblen, Hamilton, Hancock, Hawkins, Jefferson, Johnson, Knox, Loudon, McMinn, Meigs, Monroe, Morgan, Polk, Rhea, Roane, Scott, Sevier, Sullivan, Unicoi, Union, and Washington

u. Vermont
v. Virginia
w. West Virginia
x. EST is used during winter only in these Canadian provinces (EDT during summer)

i) Nunavut – most it, except for Kugluktuk, Cambridge Bay – CST/CDT and Coral Harbor (EST all year)

ii) Ontario – most parts east of 90 West and two communities west of 90 West Shebandowan, Upsala [The rest use CST/CDT or only CST.]

iii) Quebec

7. EDT is 4 hours behind Coordinated Universal Time (UTC). An email sent from someone in the EDT time zone will have the time zone listed as "-0400" in the header. EDT is used during the summer in same places as list for letter *a* through *x* listed in _part 6 above_, whereas EST is used during the winter.

8. CST is 6 hours behind Coordinated Universal Time (UTC). An email sent from someone in the CST time zone will have the time zone listed as "-0600" in the header. CST is used during winter in these places (CDT during summer):

a. Alabama
b. Arkansas
c. Florida - North-West parts

Bay, Calhoun, Escambia, Holmes, Jackson, Okaloosa, Santa Rosa, Walton and Washington counties and northern Gulf county

d. Illinois
e. Indiana - these few north-western counties near Chicago

Lake, Porter, La Porte, Newton, Jasper, Starke

and these south-western counties in Indiana near Evansville

Knox, Daviess, Gibson, Pike, Dubois, Posey, Vanderburgh, Warrick, Perry

f. Iowa
g. Kansas - except these western counties

   Greeley, Hamilton, Sherman and Wallace – MST/MDT

h. Kentucky - Western part

   Adair, Allen, Ballard, Barren, Breckinridge, Butler, Caldwell, Calloway, Carlisle, Christian, Clinton, Crittenden, Cumberland, Daviess, Edmonson, Fulton, Graves, Grayson, Green, Hansock, Hart, Henderson, Hickman, Hopkins, Livingston, Logan, Lyon, Marshall, McCracken, McLean, Metcalfe, Monroe, Muhlenberg, Ohio, Russell, Simpson, Todd, Trigg, Union, Warren and Webster counties

i. Louisiana
j. Michigan - A few western counties

   Dickinson, Gogebic, Iron, and Menominee

k. Minnesota
l. Mississippi
m. Missouri
n. Nebraska - Eastern parts

   All except Arthur, Banner, Box Butte, Chase, Cheyenne, Dawes, Deuel, Dundy, Garden, Grant, Hooker, Keith, Kimball, Morrill, Perkins, Scotts Bluff, Sheridan, and Sioux counties and the western part of Cherry county which are on MST/MDT

o. North Dakota - North and Eastern parts

   counties of Barnes, Benson, Bottineau, Burke, Burleigh, Cass, Cavalier, Dickey, Divide, Eddy, Emmons, Foster, Grand Forks, Griggs, Kidder, Lamoure, Logan, McHenry, McIntosh, McLean, Mountrail, Nelson, Oliver, Pembina, Pierce, Ramsey, Ransom, Renville, Richland, Rolette, Sargent, Sheridan, Steele, Stutsman, Towner, Traill, Walsh, Ward, Wells, Williams and northern parts of McKenzie and Dunn, westernmost part of Morton and Fort Yates in Sioux

p. Oklahoma
q. South Dakota - Eastern parts

   counties of Aurora, Beadle, Bon Homme, Brookings, Brown, Brule, Buffalo, Campbell, Charles Mix, Clark, Clay, Codington, Davison, Day, Deuel, Douglas, Edmunds, Faulk, Grant, Gregory, Hamlin, Hand, Hanson, Hughes, Hutchinson, Hyde, Jerauld, Kingsbury, Lake, Lincoln, Lyman, Marshall, McCook, McPherson, Miner, Minnehaha, Moody, Potter, Roberts, Spink, Sanborn, Sully, Tripp, Turner, Union, Yankton, Walworth and eastern parts of Jones and Stanley

r. Tennessee - Western part

counties of Bedford, Benton, Bledsoe, Cannon, Carroll, Cheatham, Chester, Clay, Coffee, Crockett, Cumberland, Davidson, Decatur, DeKalb, Dickson, Dyer, Fayette, Fentress, Franklin, Gibson, Giles, Grundy, Hardeman, Hardin, Haywood, Henderson, Henry, Hickman, Houston, Humphreys, Jackson, Lake, Lauderdale, Lawrence, Lewis, Lincoln, McNairy, Macon, Madison, Marion, Marshall, Maury, Montgomery, Moore, Obion, Overton, Perry, Pickett, Putnam, Robertson, Rutherford, Sequatchie, Shelby, Smith, Stewart, Sumner, Tipton, Trusdale, Van Buren, Warren, Wayne Weakley, White, Willamson, Wilson

s. Texas - All, but a few counties in west

El Paso and Hudspeth and part of Culberson

t. Wisconsin

u. CST is used during winter in these Canadian provinces (CDT during summer)

i) Manitoba

ii) Nunavut – Kugluktuk, Cambridge Bay only (other parts use EST/EDT or EST only)

iii) Ontario – most parts west of 90 West. (Parts east of 90 West is on EST/EDT)

iv) Saskatchewan – only Creighton and Denare Beach

v. CST is used during winter in these Mexican states (CDT during summer)

- Aguascalientes
- Campeche
- Chiapas
- Coahuila
- Colima
- Distrito Federal
- Durango
- Guanajuato
- Guerro
- Hidalgo
- Jalisco
- León
- Michoacán
- Morelos
- México
- Nuevo

- Oaxaca
- Ouebla
- Querétaro
- Quintana Roo
- San Luis Potosí
- Tabasco
- Tamaulipas
- Tlaxcala
- Veracruz
- Yucatán
- Zacatecas

9. CDT is 5 hours behind Coordinated Universal Time (UTC). An email sent from someone in the CDT time zone will have the time zone listed as "-0500" in the header. CDT is used during the summer in same places as list for letter *a* through *v* listed in *part 8 above*, whereas CST is used during the winter.

10. MST is 7 hours behind Coordinated Universal Time (UTC). An email sent from someone in the MST time zone will have the time zone listed as "-0700" in the header. MST is used during winter in these places (MDT during summer):

   a. Arizona - Navajo Nation only
   b. Colorado
   c. Idaho - most of the state except western counties

      Benewah, Bonner, Boundary, Clearwater, Kootenai, Latah, Lewis, Nez Perce, Shoshone and north part of Idaho

   d. Kansas - some western counties only

      Greeley, Hamilton, Sherman and Wallace

   e. Montana
   f. Nebraska - western counties

      Arthur, Banner, Box Butte, Chase, Cheyenne, Dawes, Deuel, Dundy, Garden, Grant, Hooker, Keith, Kimball, Morrill, Perkins, Scotts Bluff, Sheridan, and Sioux and the western part of Cherry

   g. New Mexico
   h. North Dakota - South-Western parts

counties of Adams, Billings, Bowman, Golden Valley, Grant, Hettinger, Mercer, Slope and Stark, and southern parts of Dunn and McKenzie, most of Morton and Sioux counties

i.   Oregon - parts of Malheur county only

     rest of Oregon is PST/PDT

j.   South Dakota - western counties

     Bennett, Butte, Corson, Custer, Dewey, Fall River, Haakon, Harding, Jackson, Lawrence, Meade, Mellette, Pennington, Perkins, Shannon, Todd, and Ziebach, and the western parts of Jones and Stanley

k.   Texas - a few counties in west

     El Paso and Hudspeth and part of Culberson

l.   Utah
m.   Wyoming

n.   MST is used during winter in these Canadian provinces (MDT during summer):

     i)   Alberta

     ii) British Columbia – a few eastern communities (Cranbrook, Golden, Invermere)

     iii) Northwest Territories

     iv) Saskatchewan – only Lloydminster

o.   MST is used during winter in these Mexican states (MDT during the summer):

     i)   Baja California
     ii) Cgihuahua
     iii) Nayarit
     iv) Sinaloa

11. MDT is 6 hours behind Coordinated Universal Time (UTC). An email sent from someone in the MDT time zone will have the time zone listed as "-0600" in the header. MDT is used during the summer in same places as list for letter *a* through *o* listed in _part 10 above_, whereas MST is used during the winter.

12. PST is 8 hours behind Coordinated Universal Time (UTC). An email sent from someone in the PST time zone will have the time zone listed as "-0800" in the

header. PST is used during winter in these places (PDT during summer):

a. California
b. Idaho - western counties

   Benewah, Bonner, Boundary, Clearwater, Kootenai, Latah, Lewis, Nez Perce, Shoshone and north part of Idaho

c. Nevada
d. Oregon - except most of Malheur county
e. Washington
f. PST is used during winter in these Canadian provinces (PDT during summer):
g. British Columbia - except for these eastern communities

   - Cranbrook, Golden, Invermere which is in the MST/MDT zone
   - Yukon

h. PST is used during winter in the Mexican state of Baja California Norte (PDT during summer).

13. PDT is 7 hours behind Coordinated Universal Time (UTC). An email sent from someone in the PDT time zone will have the time zone listed as "-0700" in the header. PDT is used during the summer in same places as list for letter *a* through *h* listed in *part 12 above*, whereas PST is used during the winter.

14. AKST is 9 hours behind Coordinated Universal Time (UTC). An email sent from someone in the AKST time zone will have the time zone listed as "-0900" in the header. AKST is used during winter in these places (AKDT during summer):

   a. Alaska – most, except Aleutian Islands west of 169.30 West (which use HAST/HADT)

15. AKDT is 8 hours behind Coordinated Universal Time (UTC). An email sent from someone in the AKDT time zone will have the time zone listed as "-0800" in the header. AKDT is used during summer in these places (AKST during winter):

   a. Alaska – most, except Aleutian Islands west of 169.30 West (which use HAST/HADT)

16. HAST is 10 hours behind Coordinated Universal Time (UTC). An email sent from someone in the HAST time zone will have the time zone listed as "-1000" in the header. HAST is used during winter in these US states (HADT during the summer):

   a. Hawaii
   b. Alaska – Aleutian Islands west of 169.30 West (east of 169.30 West use

AKST/AKDT)

17. HADT is 9 hours behind Coordinated Universal Time (UTC). An email sent from someone in the HADT time zone will have the time zone listed as "-0900" in the header. HADT is used during summer in these US states (HAST during the winter):

a. Hawaii
b. Alaska – Aleutian Islands west of 169.30 West (east of 169.30 West use AKST/AKDT)

CHAPTER 9
Graphing

CHAPTER 9
GRAPHING

9.1 PRESENTING DATA

After data are collected, it must be presented in a meaningful manner. One way to present data is to use the line graph. A line graph displays the relationship that exists between two quantities. This visual representation is appealing to anyone working with numerical data such as graphs that show trends, discontinuities, and other characteristics that a list of numbers cannot show. Graphs assist the reader in understanding a relationship. Like the saying, "A picture is worth a thousand words."

Many circuits or components can be better understood with a visual graph. The importance of graphs will not be stressed in your study of DC circuits, but will be widely used to illustrate circuit actions in AC circuits where RLC circuits and the oscilloscope are prevalent.

9.2 GRAPH FUNDAMENTALS

A circle of any size can be divided into four parts (quadrants) by the x-axis and y-axis. Quadrants are the divisions of a circle. This is shown in Figure 9-1. The horizontal line through the circle is called the *x*-axis. The vertical line through the circle is called the *y*-axis.

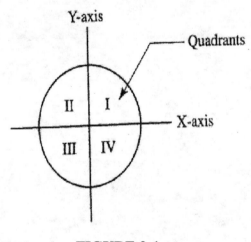

FIGURE 9-1

Furthermore, a circle can be divided into 360 degrees, 90 degrees for each quadrant. In other words, four quadrants of 90 degrees make up a complete circle. This is shown in Figure 9-2. The center of the circle where the axes cross is called the *origin*. The *origin* is the zero reference point for all measurements.

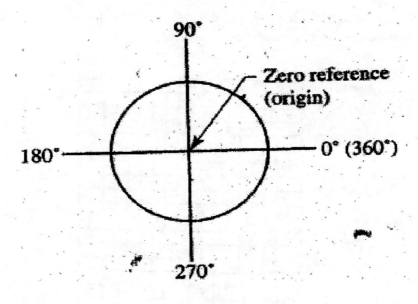

FIGURE 9-3

Each of the axes and quadrants has a polarity, as shown in Figure 9-3. From the origin, the polarity of the x-axis is positive to the right and negative to the left. The y-axis is positive toward the top and negative toward the bottom.

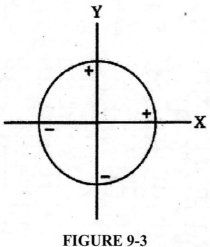

FIGURE 9-3

The data you will collect in the laboratory will often be the result of changing one variable and recording the change in another. The variable you control is called the independent variable. The data for this variable are always placed on the x-axis (horizontal axis, or abscissa). The other variable is called the dependent variable because its change is dependent on the change of the independent variable. If the two quantities under study are not related, a graph will show no relationship. Usually, we experiment only with variables that obviously depend on the independent variable.

Figure 9-4 shows the change in melting point versus specific gravity for a chemistry experiment. These two quantities are apparently not related.

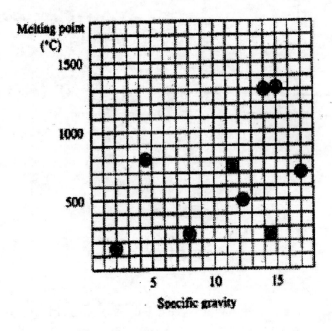

FIGURE 9-4

Figure 9-5 shows the results of an experiment conducted in an electric circuits laboratory of current versus voltage drop across a resistor. These quantities are linearly related.

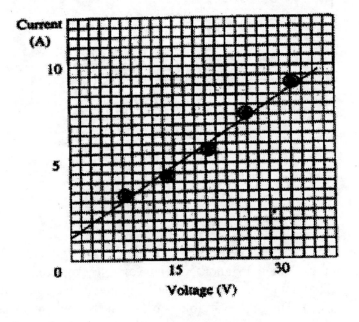

FIGURE 9-5

Figure 9-6 shows the change in distance versus time with constant acceleration from a transportation report. These quantities are exponentially related.

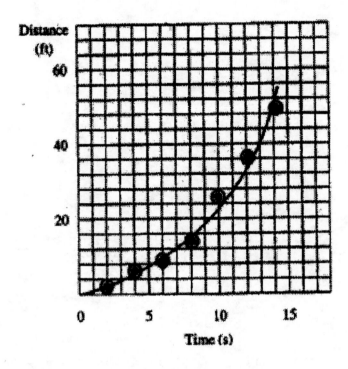

FIGURE 9-6

Figure 9-7 depicts the change in population of the world with respect to time. In this graph, time is the independent variable and belongs on the x-axis. Time is independent of population change. These quantities are exponentially related.

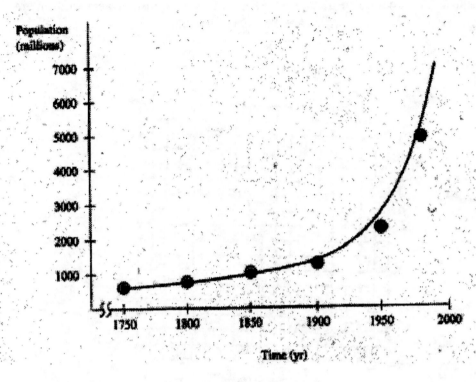

FIGURE 9-7

You may be asked to prepare or interpret graphs describing more than one relationship for an independent variable. For example in Figure 9-8, a motor's shaft power (horsepower) under load is examined. The motor's shaft power is the independent variable. The line graph illustrates multiple relationships to the one independent variable. Note that the data points for each line are plotted with a different symbol, for instance circles, squares, and triangles.

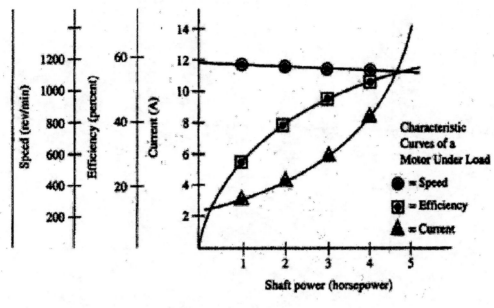

FIGURE 9-8

9.3 PLOTTING POINTS ON A SYSTEM OF RECTANGULAR COORDINATES

Consider the graph in Figure 9-9. This graph is the layout of the *Cartesian Coordinate System*. This rectangular system uses the x-axis for the horizontal direction and the y-axis for the vertical direction. The point where the *x*-axis (horizontal axis) and the *y*-axis (the vertical axis) intersect (cross) is called the *origin*. Notice that the origin is zero for both vertical and horizontal axes. Along the horizontal or *x*-axis, positive values are plotted to the right of the origin and negative values are plotted to the left of the origin. Along the vertical, or *y*-axis, positive values are plotted from the origin upward and negative values are plotted from the origin downward. The graph is divided into equal parts or divisions. The value of each division depends on the requirements of the problem. In Figure 9-9(a), the value of each division both horizontally and vertically is 1. In Figure 9-9(b), the value of each division both horizontally and vertically is 5.

171

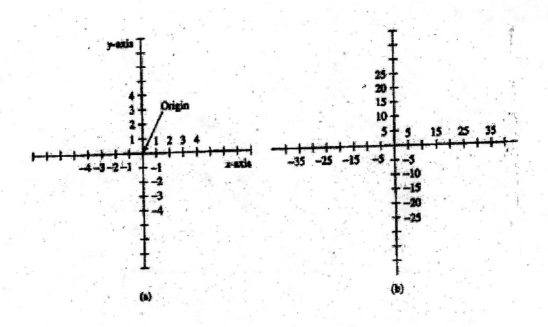

FIGURE 9-9

Let's identify some points using the graph of Figure 9-10. Locating points on a graph is done by locating the values for *x* and *y*. That is, we give values or coordinates to *x* and *y*.

Suppose that we want to identify a point whose coordinates are (-8,6). The first number identifies the horizontal or *x* value and the second number identifies the vertical or *y* value. The *x*-coordinate is called the *abscissa*. The *y*-coordinate is called the *ordinate*. The point is located by moving 8 units to the left along the *x*-axis because the number is negative. We move 6 units up along the *y*-axis because the number is positive. Draw a dashed line from each of these values. The place where the two dashed lines cross is point A.

Secondly, suppose that we want to identify a point whose coordinates are (5.5,3). The point is located by moving 5.5 units to the right along the *x*-axis because the number is positive. We move 3 units up along the *y*-axis because the number is positive. Draw a dashed line from each of these values. The place where the two dashed lines cross is point B.

Thirdly, suppose that we want to identify a point whose coordinates are (3,-6). The point is located by moving 3 units to the right along the *x*-axis because the number is positive. We move 6 units down along the *y*-axis because the number is negative. Draw a dashed line from each of these values. The place where the two dashed lines cross is point C.

172

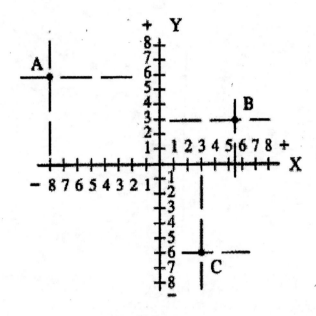

FIGURE 9-10

9.4 PLOTTING POINTS ON A SYSTEM OF POLAR COORDINATES

Another term used for point notation is *polar notation*. In trigonometry, it is written as radius and angle (r, $\angle$). An angle is identified by the Greek letter theta (θ). For instance, in Figure 9-11, the polar notation for the figure shown is $6 \angle 42°$

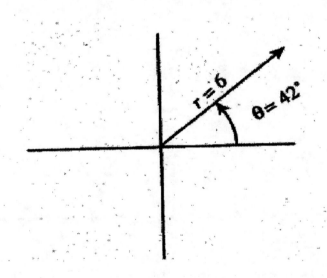

FIGURE 9-11

From examining Figure 9-12, an angle in the first quadrant is a positive theta, and an angle in the fourth quadrant is a negative theta. A positive angle ($+\theta$) goes toward the positive side of the Y-axis. A negative angle (-θ) goes toward the negative side of the Y-axis.

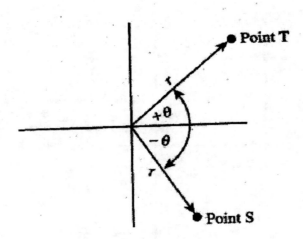

FIGURE 9-12

9.5 LINEAR AND NONLINEAR GRAPHS

Graphs can also be linear and nonlinear, as shown in Figure 9-13. Graph A is a linear graph. Graph B is a nonlinear graph. In Electronics, the x-axis is used for time or frequency. The y-axis is used for voltage, current, charge, energy, or power.

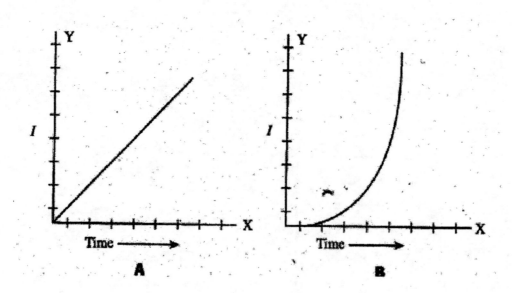

FIGURE 9-13

Linear pertains to a straight line. Values on the *x*-axis and *y*-axis change equally. In the linear graph, the line showing a rise or fall in output-to-input is straight. This ratio of rise-to-input or fall-to-input is straight.

Nonlinear graphs do not stay the same throughout a given time, resistance, or temperature, etc. In the nonlinear graphs, the rise-to-input or fall-to-input is not the same in all parts of the graph.

Nonlinear graphs are useful for illustrating direct and alternating current, as shown in Figure 9-14. Graph A depicts direct current. Graph B depicts alternating current.

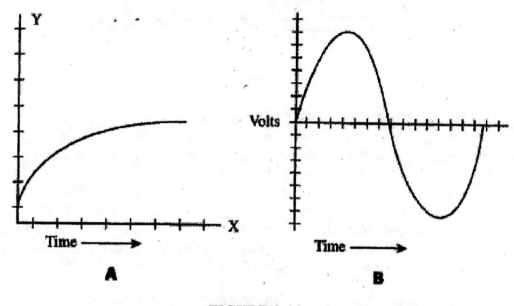

FIGURE 9-14

The standard oscilloscope has a special calibrated screen called a *graticule*, which is shown in Figure 9-15. The *graticule* is divided into one centi-meter squares. The *x*-axis is divided into ten major divisions for time, and the *y*-axis is divided into eight major divisions for voltages. The oscilloscope can be used for plotting both direct and alternating voltage, but is used more for the latter.

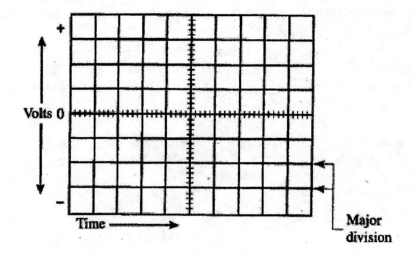

FIGURE 9-15

9.6 GRAPHING LINEAR EQUATIONS

Linear equations are equations in which a term contains only *one variable*. Furthermore, the variable exponent is 1. For example, $3x + 6 = 12$, $y - 4 = 0$, and $1 + 6t = 25$ are all linear equations. $2x + 3y = 15$ is a linear equation. Even though the variables x and y are different, they appear in different terms. $x + 6 + 7y + 8z = 20$ would be a linear equation because no term contains more than one variable. $5xy + 9 = 0$ and $2x^2 + 18 = 30$ are not linear equations. In the first equation one term contains two variables (x and y). In the second equation one of the variables is squared ($2x^2$).

Linear equations are polynomials of the 1st degree. The graph of any linear equation is a straight line.

Example 9-1

Plot the equation $2x - y = 6$ over the interval [0,2,3,5].

SOLUTION

$y = 2x - 6$

$y(0) = [2{\times}0] - 6 = 0 - 6 = -6$

$y(2) = [2{\times}2] - 6 = 4 - 6 = -2$

$y(3) = [2{\times}3] - 6 = 6 - 6 = 0$

$y(5) = [2{\times}5] - 6 = 10 - 6 = 4$

The x and y values are tabulated in Table 9-1 below.

Table 9-1

x	y
0	-6
2	-2
3	0
5	4

Graph is sketched in Figure 9-16.

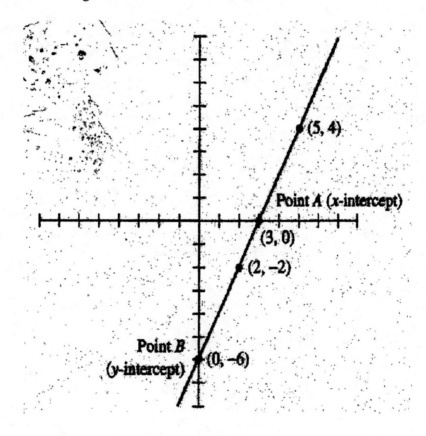

FIGURE 9-16

The x-intercept is where a line graph crosses the x-axis. The y-intercept is where a line graph crosses the y-axis.

Example 9-2

What are the x-intercept and y-intercept of Example 9-1?

SOLUTION

x-intercept: (3,0)

y-intercept: (0,-6)

Example 9-3

Plot the function $f(t) = t + 1$ over the interval [-3,3] and identify the x-intercept and y-intercept.

SOLUTION

The interval from -3 to 3 will be divided into increments of 1 [-3, -2, -1, 0, 1, 2, 3].

$f(-3) = -3 + 1 = -2$

$f(-2) = -2 + 1 = -1$

$f(-1) = -1 + 1 = 0$

$f(0) = 0 + 1 = 1$

$f(1) = 1 + 1 = 2$

$f(2) = 2 + 1 = 3$

$f(3) = 3 + 1 = 4$

The t and f values are tabulated in Table 9-2 below.

TABLE 9-2

t	$f(t)$
-3	-2
-2	-1
-1	0
0	1
1	2
2	3
3	4

x-intercept: (-1,0)

y-intercept: (0,1)

Graph is sketched in Figure 9-17.

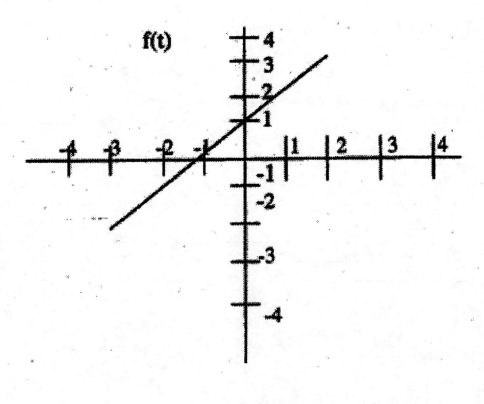

GRAPH 9-17

Example 9-4

Plot the function $y - 2x = 2$ over the interval [-3,-1,0,2] and identify the *x*-intercept and *y*-intercept.

SOLUTION

$y = 2x + 2$

$y(-3) = [2 \times -3] + 2 = -6 + 2 = -4$

$y(-1) = [2 \times -1] + 2 = -2 + 2 = 0$

$y(0) = [2 \times 0] + 2 = 0 + 2 = 2$

$y(2) = [2 \times 2] + 2 = 4 + 2 = 6$

The x and y values are tabulated in Table 9-3 below.

TABLE 9-3

x	y
-3	-4
-1	0
0	2
2	6

x-intercept: (-1,0)

y-intercept: (0,2)

Graph is sketched in Figure 9-18.

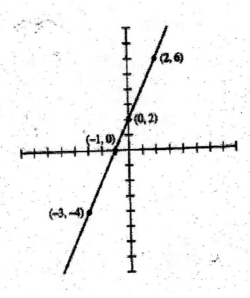

FIGURE 9-18

The slope of a line is defined as the change in y that results from an increase in x.

$$\text{Slope} = \frac{\Delta y}{\Delta x} = \frac{\text{change in } y}{\text{change in } x}$$

When we read a graph, we always make Δx positive. The resulting Δy will be either positive or negative depending on whether y increased or decreased as x increased. The slope is positive if Δy is positive or negative if Δy is negative.

Figure 9-19(a) shows a positive slope line. Figure 9-19(b) shows a negative slope line.

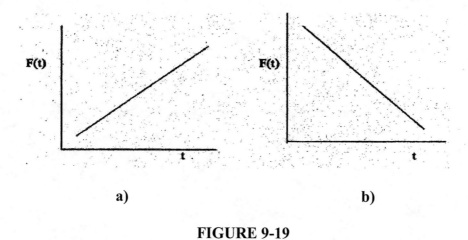

a)   b)

FIGURE 9-19

The linear equation in Example 9-1 is redrawn in Figure 9-20. Consider the point (3,0). If x is changed from 3 to 5, y changes from 0 to 4. The change in x is 2. This would be written $\Delta x = 2$ (delta $x = 2$). The change in y is 4. This would be written $\Delta y = 4$ (delta $y = 4$). Upon inspection of the curve, we find that for any increase of 2 units horizontally ($\Delta x = 2$), y increases 4 units ($\Delta y = 4$). For example, if x increases from -2 units to 0, y increases from -10 units to -6 units. If x increases from 1 unit to 3 units, y increases from -4 units to 0.

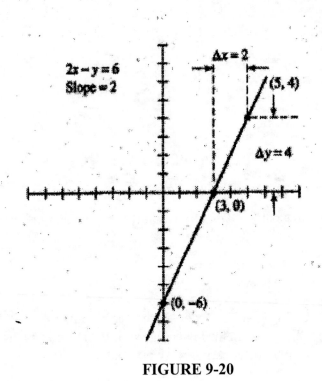

FIGURE 9-20

The slope, then is:

$$\frac{\Delta y}{\Delta x} = \frac{2}{1} = 2$$

That is, any increase of 1 unit in the value of x causes a 2 unit increase in the value of y.

Example 9-5

Consider the straight line in Figure 9-21 which results from the equation $x + 2y = 4$. Find the slope of the line, x-intercept and y-intercept.

SOLUTION

If x increases from 0 to 4 ($\Delta x = 4$), y decreases from 2 to 0 ($\Delta y = -2$). Any increase in the value of x causes a corresponding decrease in the value of y in the ratio of 2 to -1. Any 4-unit increase in x causes a 2-unit decrease in y. Any 8-unit increase in x causes a 4-unit decrease in y and so on.

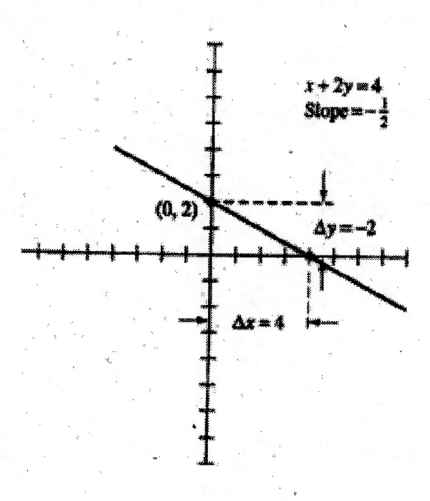

FIGURE 9-21

183

$$\text{Slope} = \frac{\Delta y}{\Delta x} = \frac{-2}{4} = -\frac{1}{2}$$

x-intercept: $(4,0)$

y-intercept: $(0,2)$

Any linear equation containing two variables can be written in the slope-intercept form.

$$y = mx + b$$

y and x are the variables; m and b are constants. When the equation is written in this form, it is said to be written in the *slope-intercept form* because m is the slope and b is the vertical or y-intercept.

Example 9-6

Given the equation $3y - 2x = 9$, find the slope and the y-intercept.

SOLUTION

Change the equation to slope-intercept form.

$$3y - 2x = 9$$

$$3y = 2x + 9$$

$$y = \frac{2}{3}x + 3$$

The slope is $\frac{2}{3}$ and the y-intercept is 3. Thus $m = \frac{2}{3}$ and $b = 3$.

Given two points represented by the ordered pairs (x_1, y_1) and (x_2, y_2), the distance d between the points is given by

$$d = \sqrt{(x_2 - x_1)^2 + (y_2 - y_1)^2}$$

Example 9.7

Find the distance between (-4,1) and (3,-2).

SOLUTION

First, choose one ordered pair to serve as (x_1, y_1), and the other to serve as (x_2, y_2). This choice is completely arbitrary and does not affect the final result.

$(x_1, y_1) = (-4, 1)$

$(x_2, y_2) = (3, -2)$

$x_1 = -4 \quad y_1 = 1 \quad x_2 = 3 \quad y_2 = -2$

$$d = \sqrt{(x_2 - x_1)^2 + (y_2 - y_1)^2}$$

$$d = \sqrt{(3 - (-4))^2 + (-2 - 1)^2}$$

$$d = \sqrt{7^2 + (-3)^2}$$

$$d = \sqrt{7^2 + 3^2}$$

$$d = \sqrt{49 + 9}$$

$$d = \sqrt{58}$$

$d = 7.616$

The midpoint of a line segment is the point halfway between two endpoints. The midpoint is given by the following formula:

$$\left(\frac{x_1 + x_2}{2}, \frac{y_1 + y_2}{2} \right)$$

Figure 9-22 shows the midpoint of a line segment.

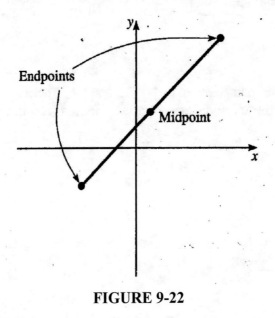

FIGURE 9-22

Example 9-8 Find the midpoint of the line segment joining (1,-1) and (-2, 4).

SOLUTION

$x_1 = 1$ $y_1 = -1$ $x_2 = -2$ $y_2 = 4$

$$\left(\frac{x_1 + x_2}{2}, \frac{y_1 + y_2}{2} \right) = \left(\frac{1-2}{2}, \frac{-1+4}{2} \right)$$

The midpoint is given by $\left(\frac{-1}{2}, \frac{3}{2} \right)$.

9.7 GRAPHING NONLINEAR EQUATIONS

Nonlinear equations are polynomials of the 2nd degree and higher. Nonlinear equations are very popular in the science, engineering and technology. The most popular nonlinear equations are the sinusoidal and non-sinusoidal waveforms. The graphs of these waveforms are shown in Figure 9-23.

186

SINUSOIDAL WAVEFORMS

Sine Wave

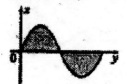

Cosine Wave

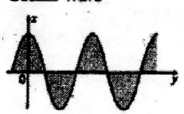

NONSINUSOIDAL WAVEFORMS

DC Wave

Square Wave

Triangular Wave

Sawtooth Wave

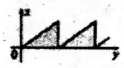

Rectified Wave

FIGURE 9-23

187

Example 9-9

Plot the function $f(t) = 2t^2 + 8t + 1$ over the interval [-4,-3,-2,-1,0,1,2].

SOLUTION

$f(-4) = 2(-4)^2 + 8(-4) + 1 = 1$

$f(-3) = 2(-3)^2 + 8(-3) + 1 = -5$

$f(-2) = 2(-2)^2 + 8(-2) + 1 = -7$

$f(-1) = 2(-1)^2 + 8(-1) + 1 = -5$

$f(0) = 2(0)^2 + 8(0) + 1 = 1$

$f(1) = 2(1)^2 + 8(1) + 1 = 1$

$f(2) = 2(2)^2 + 8(2) + 1 = 25$

The t and f values are tabulated in Table 9-4 below.

GRAPH TABLE 9.4

t	$f(t)$
-4	1
-3	-5
-2	-7
-1	-5
0	1
1	11
2	25

Graph is sketched in Figure 9-24.

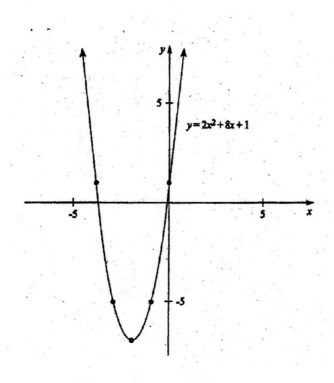

$y = 2x^2 + 8x + 1$

FIGURE 9-24

9.8 SELECTING SCALES FOR GRAPHS

How you interpret a graph will depend on the type of scale used as well as the numerical division of the scale. The same information presented on two types of graph scales appears very different. Both graphs in Figure 9-25 are based on the same information; however, the numerical scales are different. Graph A is scaled in units of ten, and Graph B is scaled in units of one. Smaller increments usually lead to more detailed graphs. The graphs are visually different even though they contain the same information. Lack of a zero reference tends to distort the appearance of graphs too.

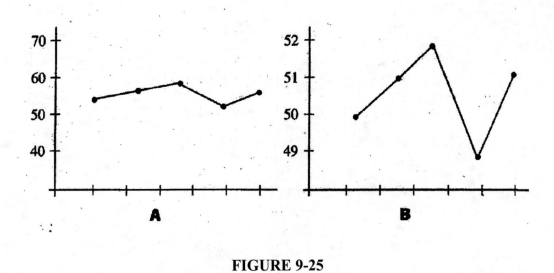

FIGURE 9-25

Figure 9-26 shows that the type of scale is just as important as the numerical scale. Part A, Part B, and Part C are linear scales. In a linear scale, the distance from one major division to another is equal.

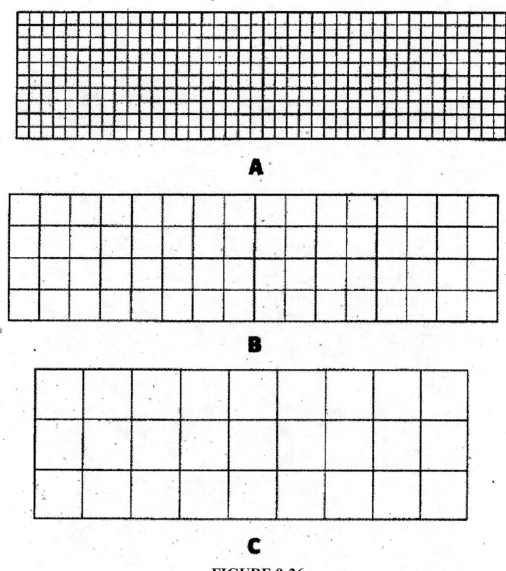

FIGURE 9-26

Part A has ten units per inch. The major divisions of the graph are one-inch squares, and each small division is in tenths (1/10).

Part B has units that are ¼ inch each. The divisions of the graph are also one inch for each major division, but the smaller divisions are ¼.

Part C has units that are 1 cm each. There are no small divisions in this scale, but the distance from one division to another is the same, indicating a linear scale.

Semi-logarithmic graph paper is used for making a response curve of electronic circuits. Figure 9-27 depicts a semi-logarithmic graph paper with three cycles. Figure 9-28 depicts a semi-logarithmic graph paper with four cycles. A semi-log graph has a linear scale across the bottom, but the vertical axis is nonlinear. The distance from point 1 to point 2 is different than the distance from point 2 to point 3. Semi-log graph scale comes in 2-, 3-, 4-, 5-, and 7 cycle grids.

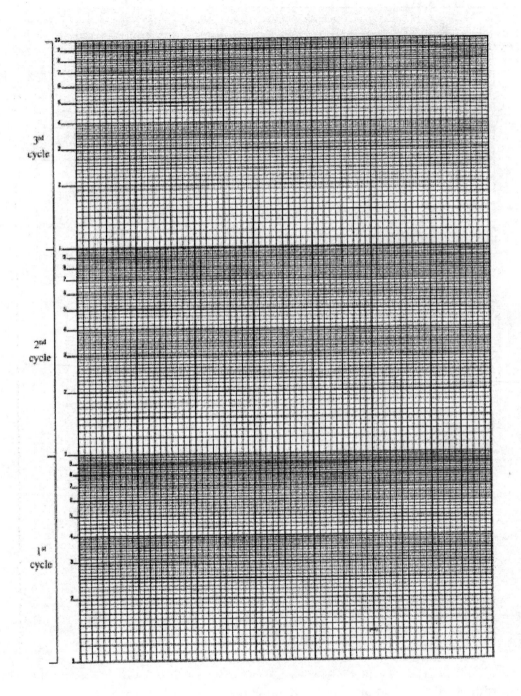

FIGURE 9-27

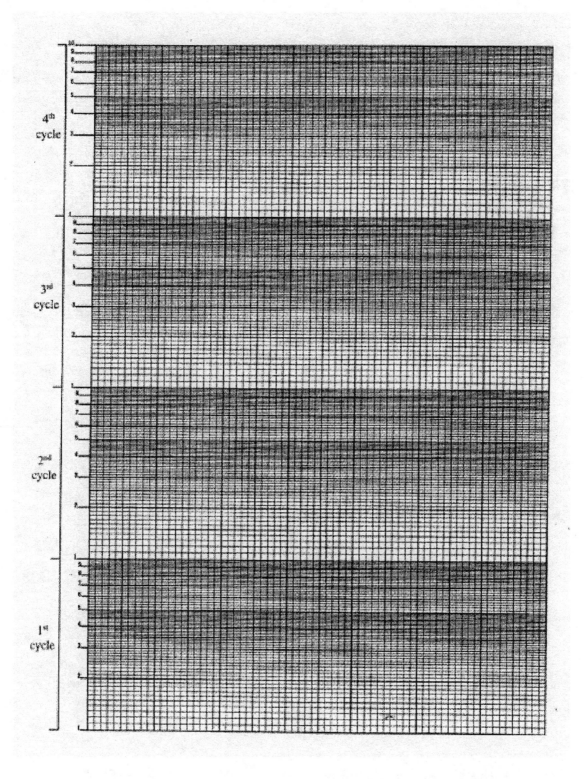

FIGURE 9-28

Figure 9-29 depicts full logarithmic graph paper. This type of graph paper is also referred to as log-log paper because it has a log-log scale. This type of graph paper is logarithmic in both vertical and horizontal directions. There is no linear scale on this type of graph paper.

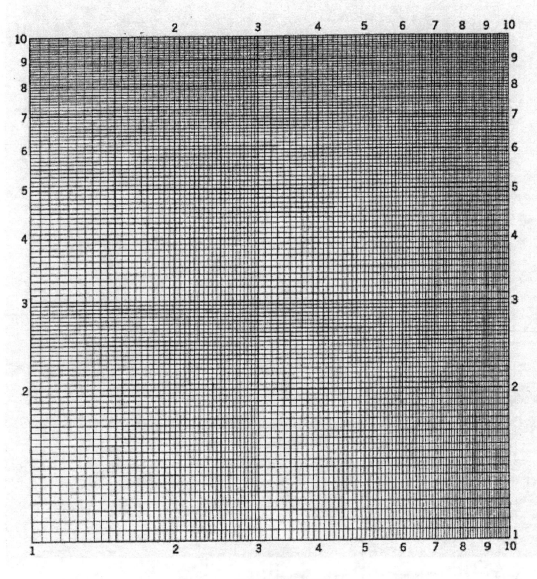

FIGURE 9-29

Certain types of graphs, such as antenna radiation patterns, microphone pickup patterns, or vector displays, require the use of a polar coordinate graph scale. A polar coordinate graph sheet is shown in Figure 9-30.

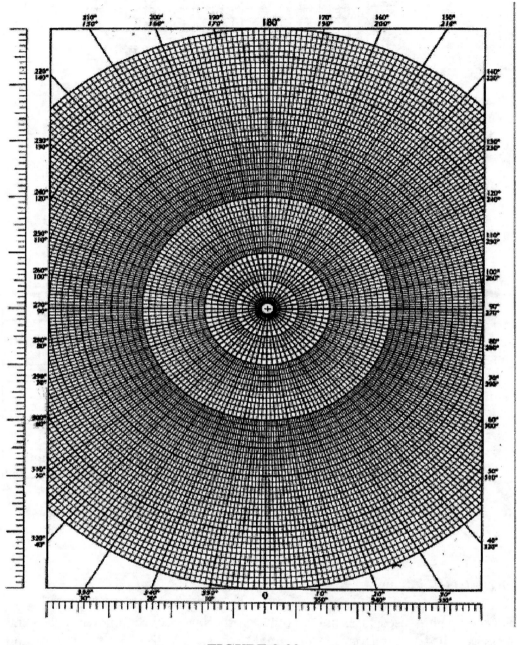

FIGURE 9-30

Curved graphs (e.g., exponential and inverse functions) can be straightened by using semi-logarithmic (semi-log) or logarithmic (log-log) graph paper.

Suppose that a tool's life depends on its cutting speed. Figure 9-31(a) illustrates the nonlinear output on regular graph paper. Figure 9-31(b) shows semi-logarithmic paper yields a straight-line graph.

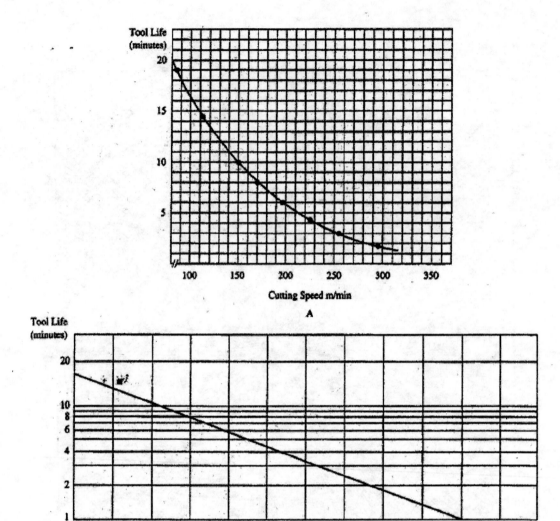

FIGURE 9-31

9.9 INTERPOLATION

When the graph is used to examine points on the line between known data points, the process is called interpolation. If the graph is a straight-line graph, interpolation is a simple process. You can use a straight ruler. Figure 9-32(a) shows the straight-line interpolation.

Interpolation of data along a curved line is more difficult. The curved line is at your best estimate of what the line should look like. Extracting information between known points on a curved line is an estimate. Figure 9-32(b) shows curved-line interpolation of an exponential function.

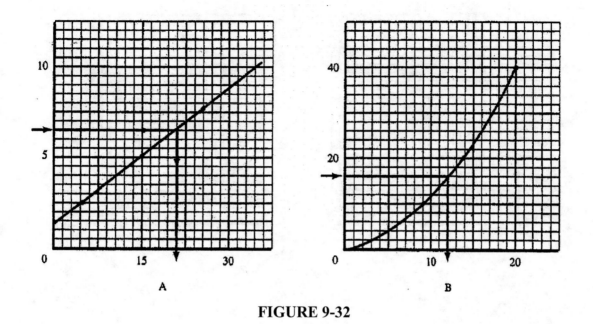

FIGURE 9-32

9.10 EXTRAPOLATION

Estimating the curve's fit beyond the experimental data points is known as extrapolation. Again, a straight-line graph will offer easy and usually reliable results. You can use a straight ruler. Figure 9-33(a) shows straight-line extrapolation.

Extending a curved line such as an exponential function requires greater skill. A template, such as a French curve is useful to sketch both smooth and irregular curves for best fit and curved-line extension. Figure 9-33(b) shows curved-line extrapolation of an exponential function.

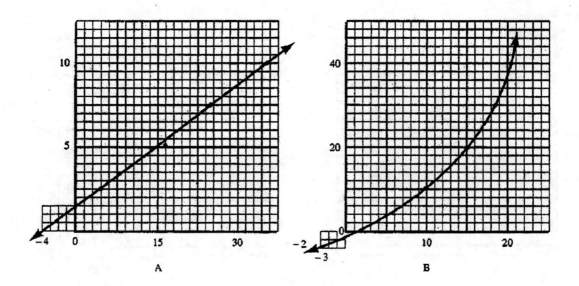

A

B

FIGURE 9-33

When using a French curve, try to keep the instrument on at least three points as you draw the line. If there is too much blank space between the points, you may need to gather more data to place between the points to ensure the curve is correct. Figure 9-34 shows a picture of a French curve instrument. Notice that it allows at least three points of contact.

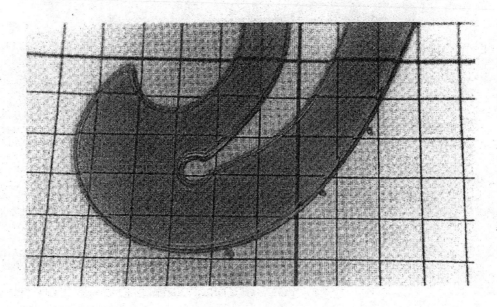

FIGURE 9-34

9.11 USING MATLAB FOR PLOTTING TWO-DIMENSIONAL GRAPHICS

The plot FUNCTION

1. The common function for plotting 2-D data is the plot function. This versatile function plots sets of data arrays on appropriate axes and connects points with straight lines.

Example 9-10 Use MATLAB to plot the sine wave over the interval $0 \leq x \leq 2\pi$. Label x values on the *x*-axis. Label y values on the *y*-axis. Label the title of this graph, *The Sine Wave*.

SOLUTION

\>> x = linspace (0,2*pi,30);

Press <u>enter</u> on the keyboard.

This line command creates 30 data points over $0 \leq x \leq 2\pi$ to form the horizontal axis of the plot.

NOTE: Retype the command >> x = linspace (0,2*pi,30), without the semicolon. MATLAB will show the 30 data points computed.

The syntax for linspace is linespace (first_value, last_value, number_of_values). In this example, the MATLAB function linspace is used to create *x*. x = linspace (0,2*pi,30) is an array construction technique creates a linearly spaced row vector *x* starting with, ending at last, and having *n* elements.

\>> y = sin (x);

Press <u>enter</u> on the keyboard.

This line command creates another vector *y* containing the sine of the data points in *x*.

NOTE: Retype the command >> y = sin(x) without the semicolon. MATLAB will show the computed data points for *y*.

\>> plot (x,y)

Press <u>enter</u> on the keyboard.

The plot function opens a graphics window called Figure, scales the axes to fit the data, plots the points, and then connects the points with straight lines.

>> title ('The Sine Wave')

Press <u>enter</u> on the keyboard.

This command gives the graph a title.

>> xlabel ('x values')

Press <u>enter</u> on the keyboard.

This command labels the x-axis.

>> ylabel ('y values')

Press <u>enter</u> on the keyboard.

This command labels the y-axis.

The graph is shown in Figure 9-35 below.

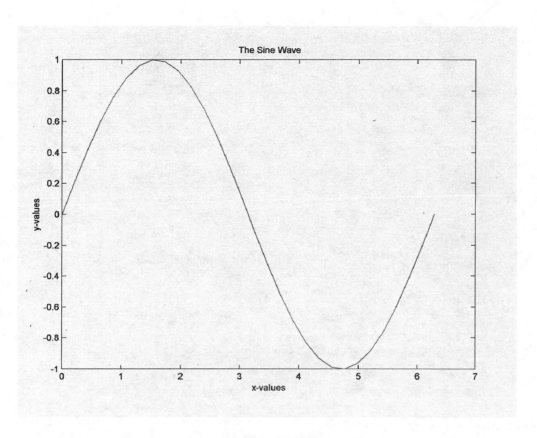

FIGURE 9-35

Example 9-11 Use MATLAB's *grid on* command on the Sine wave of Example 9-10 to view the graphical display.

SOLUTION

The *grid on* command adds grid onto the current plot at the ticks.

>> grid on

Press <u>enter</u> on the keyboard.

The graphical output is shown in Figure 9-36.

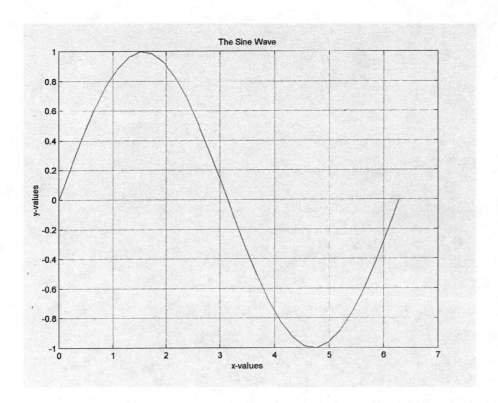

FIGURE 9-36

>> grid off

Press <u>enter</u> on the keyboard.

The *grid off* command removes the grid. The *grid off* command will convert Figure 9-36 back into Figure 9-35.

grid with no arguments alternately turns the grid lines on and off; that is, it toggles them.

You can specify your own colors, markers, and line-styles by giving a third argument after each pair of data arrays. This optional argument is a character string consisting of one or more characters from Table 9.5.

TABLE 9.5

Symbol	Color	Symbol	Marker	Symbol	Line Style
b	blue	.	point	-	solid line
g	green	o	circle	:	dotted line
r	red	x	cross	-.	dash-dot line
c	cyan	+	plus sign	--	dashed line
m	magenta	*	asterisk		
y	yellow	s	square		
k	black	d	diamond		
w	white	ˇ	triangle (down)		
		^	triangle (up)		
		<	triangle (left)		
		>	triangle (right)		
		p	pentagram		
		h	hexagram		

Example 9-12 Use MATLAB to change the color of the graph of Example 9-10 for each case below:

i)   black
ii) green
iii) red
iv) yellow

SOLUTION

i) >> plot (x,y,'k')

This line command plots the sine wave in the color black.

Press <u>enter</u> on the keyboard.

>> title('The Sine Wave'), xlabel('x-values'), ylabel('y-values')

Press <u>enter</u> on the keyboard.

Figure 9-37 shows the graphical output of the waveform.

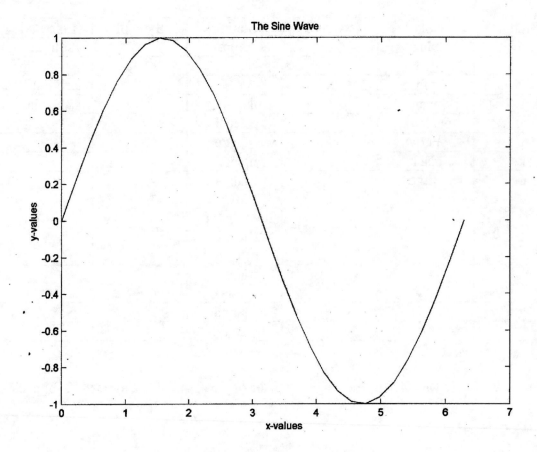

FIGURE 9-37

ii) >> plot (x,y,'g')

This line command plots the sine wave in the color green.

Press <u>enter</u> on the keyboard.

>> title('The Sine Wave'), xlabel('x-values'), ylabel('y-values')

Press <u>enter</u> on the keyboard.

Figure 9-38 shows the graphical output of the waveform.

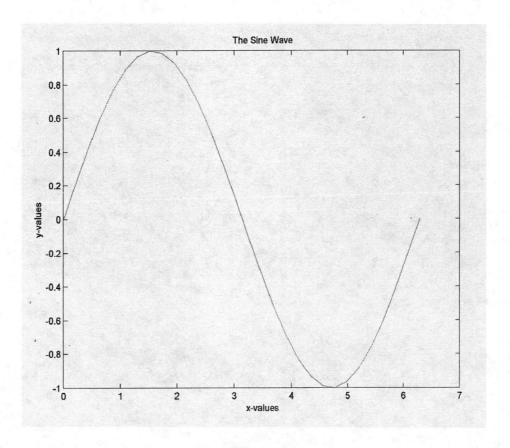

FIGURE 9-38

iii) >> plot (x,y,'r')

This line command plots the sine wave in the color red.

Press <u>enter</u> on the keyboard.

>> title('The Sine Wave'), xlabel('x-values'), ylabel('y-values')

Press <u>enter</u> on the keyboard.

Figure 9-39 shows the graphical output of the waveform.

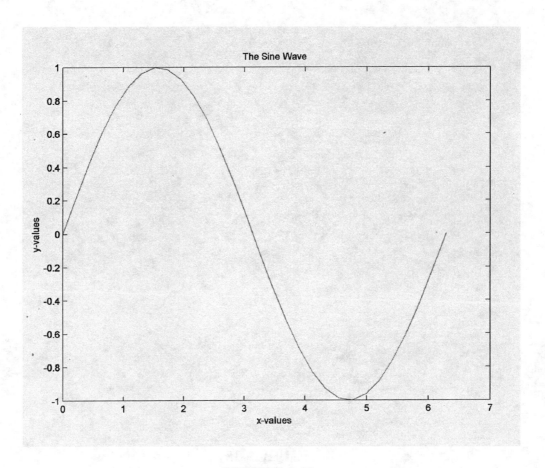

FIGURE 9-39

iii) >> plot (x,y,'y')

 This line command plots the sine wave in the color yellow.

Press <u>enter</u> on the keyboard.

>> title('The Sine Wave'), xlabel('x-values'), ylabel('y-values')

Press <u>enter</u> on the keyboard.

Figure 9-40 shows the graphical output of the waveform.

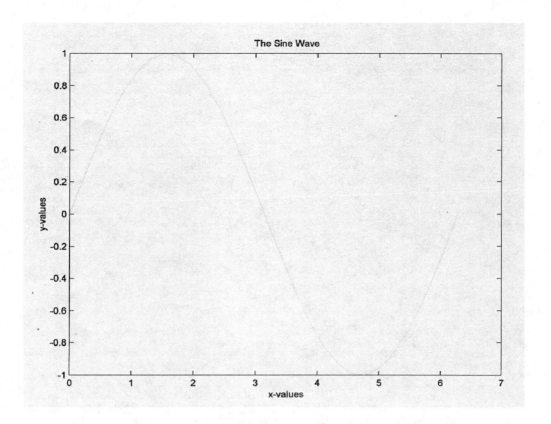

The Sine Wave

FIGURE 9-40

Example 9-13 Use MATLAB to generate the following cases for Example 9-10:

a) green sine wave with the dash line style.
b) magenta sine wave with the dash-dot line style.
c) cyan sine wave with the dotted line style.
d) blue sine wave with the solid line style.

SOLUTION

a) >> plot (x,y,'--g')

 This line command plots a dashed sine wave in the color green.

Press <u>enter</u> on the keyboard.

>> title('The Sine Wave'), xlabel('x-values'), ylabel('y-values')

Press <u>enter</u> on the keyboard.

Figure 9-41 shows the graphical output of the waveform.

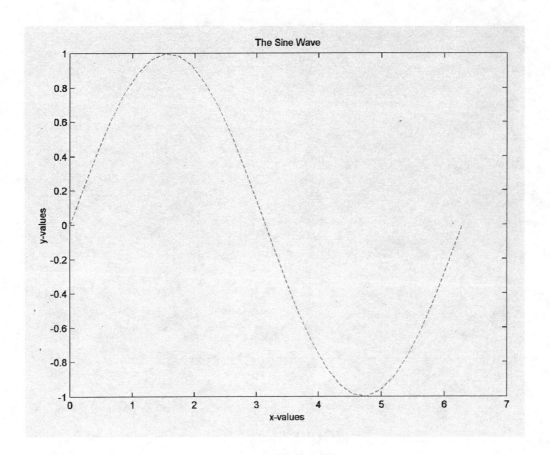

FIGURE 9-41

b) >> plot (x,y,'-.m')

 This line command plots a dash-dot sine wave in the color magenta.

Press <u>enter</u> on the keyboard.

>> title('The Sine Wave'), xlabel('x-values'), ylabel('y-values')

Press <u>enter</u> on the keyboard.

Figure 9-42 shows the graphical output of the waveform.

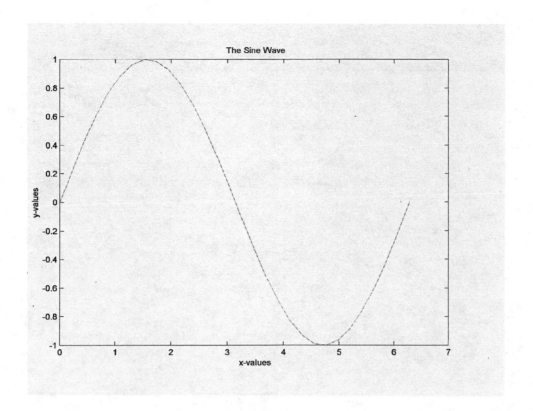

The Sine Wave

FIGURE 9-42

c) >> plot (x,y,':k')

This line command plots a dotted sine wave in the color blue.

Press <u>enter</u> on the keyboard.

>> title('The Sine Wave'), xlabel('x-values'), ylabel('y-values')

Press <u>enter</u> on the keyboard.

Figure 9-43 shows the graphical output of the waveform.

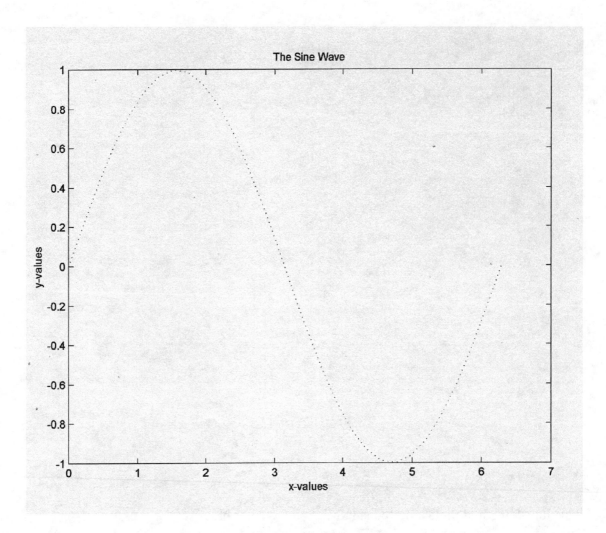

FIGURE 9-43

c) >> plot (x,y,'-b')

 This line command plots a dotted sine wave in the color blue.

Press <u>enter</u> on the keyboard.

>> title('The Sine Wave'), xlabel('x-values'), ylabel('y-values')

Press <u>enter</u> on the keyboard.

Figure 9-44 shows the graphical output of the waveform.

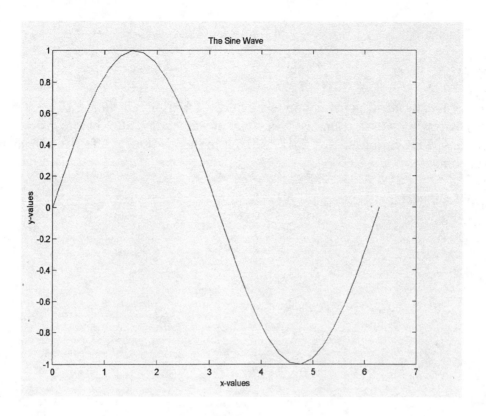

FIGURE 9-44

Case d) is the default color and the default line style in MATLAB.

Example 9-14 Use MATLAB to generate the two graphs over the interval [-3, 3] in increments of 1.

Graph 1 $y(x) = 2x$

Graph 2 $z(x) = -3x + 2$

Table 9-6 below shows the colors, line styles, and markers of the two graphs.

TABLE 9-6

Graph	Color	Line Style	Marker
Graph 1	Red	Dotted Line	Asterisk
Graph 2	Black	Dashed Line	Circle

SOLUTION

>> x = -3:1:3;

MATLAB uses the array construction technique x = *first:increment:last* to create the row vector *x* starting with first, counting by increment, and ending at or before last.
NOTE: Retype the command x = -3:1:3 without the semicolon. MATLAB will show all the data points.

MATLAB will display

    x =

        -3 -2 -1 0 1 2 3

>> y = 2*x;

Press <u>enter</u> on the keyboard.

>> z = (-3*2) + 2;

Press <u>enter</u> on the keyboard.

>> plot (x,y,'r:*',x,z,'k--o')

Press <u>enter</u> on the keyboard.

>> title('Graph 1 & Graph 2'), xlabel('x-axis'), ylabel('y-axis')

Figure 9-45 shows the outputs of graph 1 and graph 2.

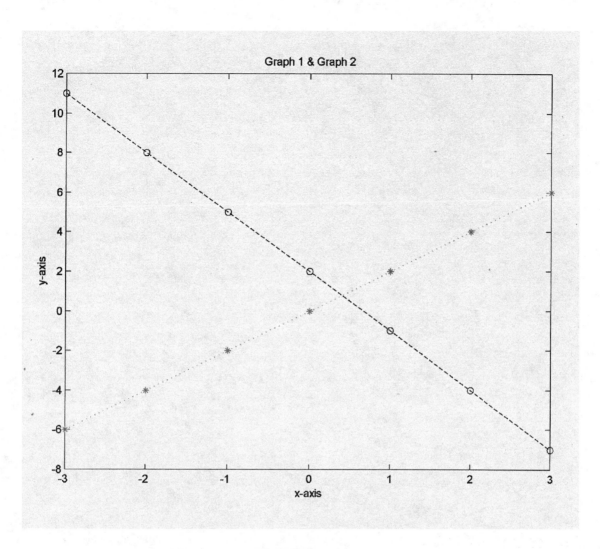

FIGURE 9-45

Stat Project — research quarter backs
get numbers for 12 weeks
season

QB   Statistics

Table A -- 2018 Data

ex.

WEEKS	comp/Att	Pass Yards	TD/Int	Fumbles Lost
1	10/15	100	1/1	0
2	5/10	200	2/0	0
3	9/12	255	3/0	1
4	3/10	175	0/3	2
5	12/15	380	4/1	1

a) compute the avg F or completed passes
by hand and MATLAB

$$avg. = \frac{10 + 5 + 9 + 3 + 12}{5} = \frac{39}{5} = 7.8$$

(lowest # u
the mode)

>> A = [10 5 9 3 12]

>> mean (A)

b) Calculate median for fumbles lost
B = [0 0 1 2 1]
median (B):

All lowercase!
Variables

calculate std

M = mean
x_i = sample point
N = total number of sample points

$$\sigma = \sqrt{\frac{\sum_i^n (x_i - N)^2}{N-1}}$$

N **214** USP SOURCES!

variance = σ^2

CHAPTER 10
Statistics

CHAPTER 10
STATISTICS

10.1 INTRODUCTION

Every day we encounter information. Information comes at us in a number of different ways and in different forms. Statistics make sense of all this information by using certain tools and ways of thinking.

The word "statistics" is used in several different senses. In the broadest sense, "statistics" refers to a range of techniques and procedures for analyzing data, interpreting data, displaying data, and making decisions based on data. This is what courses in "statistics" generally cover. In a second usage, a "statistic" is defined as a numerical quantity (such as the mean) calculated in a sample. Such statistics are used to estimate parameters.

Statistics is the study of numerical information called data. Statisticians acquire, organize, and analyze data. Each part of this process is also scrutinized. Statisticians answer the following questions:

    i)   How many calories did each of use eat for breakfast?
    ii)   How far from home did everyone travel today?
    iii)   How big is the place we call home?
    iv)   How many other people call it home?

One of the recurring themes of statistics is that we are able to say something about a large group based upon the study of a relatively small portion of that group. The group as a whole is known as the *population*. The portion of the group that we study is the *sample*. As an example of this, suppose we wanted to know the average height of people living in the United States. We could try to measure over 300 million people, but this would be infeasible. It would be a logistical nightmare to conduct the measurements in such a way that no one was missed and no one was counted twice. Due to the impossible nature of measuring everyone in the United States we could instead use statistics. Rather than finding the heights of everyone in the population, we take a statistical sample of a few thousand. If we sample the population correctly, then the average height of the sample will be very close to the average height of the population.

To draw good conclusions, we need good data to work with. Careful organization and graphical displays of the data help us to spot patterns and trends, before we actually do any calculations. Most commonly used samples:

    i)   Simple Random
    ii)   Stratified
    iii)   Clustered

Common graphs for organized data:

i)   Pie Charts or Circle Graphs
ii)   Bar or Pareto Graphs
iii)   Scatterplots
iv)   Time Plots
v)   Stem and Leaf Plots
vi)   Box and Whisker graphs

A parameter is a numerical quantity measuring some aspect of a population of data values. For example, the mean is a measure of central tendency. Greek letters are used to designate parameters. In Table 10-1 are shown several parameters of great importance in statistical analyses and the Greek symbol that represents each one. Parameters are rarely known and are usually estimated by statistics computed in samples. A sample is a subset of a population. To the right of each Greek symbol is the symbol for the associated statistic used to estimate it from a sample.

TABLE 10-1

Quantity	Parameter	Statistic
Mean	M	μ
Standard Deviation	Σ	s
Proportion	Π	p
Correlation	P	r

The term "statistics" sometimes refers to calculated quantities regardless of whether or not they are from a sample. For example, one might ask about a baseball player's statistics and be referring to his or her batting average, runs batted in, number of home runs, etc. Or, "government statistics" can refer to any numerical indexes calculated by a governmental agency.

Although the different meanings of "statistics" have the potential for confusion, a careful consideration of the context in which the word is used should make its intended meaning clear.

Statistics can be classified as descriptive statistics sand inferential statistics. In descriptive statistics, data is analyzed by calculating quantities that describe that data. The quantities of descriptive statistics include the mean, median, mode, range, variance, standard deviation, correlation and regression. The mean, median and mode are used to find the average an center of the data. The range, variance and standard deviation describe how spread out the data is. Correlation and regression are used for curve fitting. If we begin with a sample and then try to infer something about the population then we are using inferential statistics. With inferential statistics, you must establish a hypothesis first, then use statistical tools with the sample to determine the likelihood that we need to reject the hypothesis or not.

Some possible applications of statistics include:

a) Psychology
b) Economics
c) Medicine
d) Advertising
e) Demography
f) Engineering/technology

10.2 CENTRAL TENDENCY

Measures of central tendency are numbers used to represent the distribution of data. There are five measures of central tendency. They are the arithmetic mean, median, mode, trimean, and the trimmed mean.

10.2.1 ARITHMETIC MEAN

The arithmetic mean is what is commonly called the average: When the word "mean" is used without a modifier, it can be assumed that it refers to the arithmetic mean. The mean is the sum of all the data points divided by the number of data points. Of the five measures of central tendency, the mean is by far the most widely used. It takes every data point into account.

It is the most efficient measure of central tendency for normal distributions. Normal distributions are a family of distributions that have the shape shown below in
Figure 10-1.

FIGURE 10-1

Normal distributions are symmetric with data values more concentrated in the middle than in the tails. Many kinds of behavioral data are approximated well by the normal distribution. Many statistical tests assume a normal distribution. Most of these tests work well even if the distribution is only approximately normal and in many cases as long as it does not deviate greatly from normality. In the normal distribution, the mean, median, and mode are all the same.

The *Bell Curve* is another name for the normal distribution, because it is a symmetrical curve representing a normal distribution. The Bell Curve has more or less the shape of a bell. In science the Bell Curve is called the *Gaussian Curve*.

The characteristic shape of the graph of a normal distribution is called a bell-shaped curve. Figure 10-2 shows the graph of a perfect Bell-Shaped Curve. Equation 13-1 is used to graph the bell-shaped curve.

$$f(x) = \frac{1}{\sqrt{2\pi}} \exp\left(\frac{-x^2}{2}\right) \quad (10\text{-}1)$$

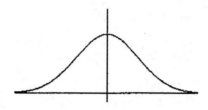

FIGURE 10-2

The mean is mathematically tractable making it possible for statisticians to develop statistical procedures for drawing inferences about means.

Given data values $x_1, x_2, x_3, \ldots, x_n$, the arithmetic mean $\bar{x}$ is given by equation 10-2

$$\bar{x} = \frac{x_1 + x_2 + x_3 + x_4 + \ldots + x_n}{n} = \frac{\sum_{i=1}^{n} x_i}{n} \quad (10\text{-}2)$$

where the Greek letter Σ (upper case sigma) denotes a sum. The notation $\sum_{i=1}^{n}$ means to add x_1, $x_2, x_3, \ldots, x_n$. The variable n equals the number of values in the data set.

Example 10-1

The monthly electrical energy consumption (in kilowatt-hours) of 8 families with the same size house was found to be

618   597   715   674   703   637   657   586

Find the average monthly energy consumption of these families.

SOLUTION

Using equation 10-2,

$$\bar{x} = \frac{\sum_{i=1}^{n} x_i}{n} = \frac{\sum_{i=1}^{8} x_i}{8} = \frac{[618 + 597 + 715 + 674 + 703 + 637 + 657 + 586]}{8} = \frac{5,187}{8} \approx 648$$

We can also calculate the arithmetic mean given a frequency distribution using equation 10-3.

$$\bar{x} = \frac{\sum_{i=1}^{n} f_i x_i}{\sum_{i=1}^{n} f_i} \qquad (10\text{-}3)$$

x_i = a data value. f_i is equal to a frequency value.

Example 10-2

A quality control technologist counted the number of defective light bulbs in lots of 100. From the following frequency distribution, determine the average numbers of defective bulbs per 100.

Number of Defective Bulbs	3	5	6	8	4
Frequency	6	2	1	2	4

SOLUTION

Using equation 10-3,

$$\bar{x} = \frac{\sum_{i=1}^{n} f_i x_i}{\sum_{i=1}^{n} f_i} = \frac{[(3 \times 6) + (5 \times 2) + (6 \times 1) + (3 \times 2) + (4 \times 4)]}{[6 + 2 + 1 + 2 + 4]} = 4.4$$

On average, there are approximately 4 defective bulbs per hundred.

10.2.2 MEDIAN

The median is the middle of a distribution: half the scores are above the median and half are below the median, when the data is arranged in numerical order in an array. The median is less sensitive to extreme scores than the mean and this makes it a better measure than the mean for highly skewed distributions.

A distribution is skewed if one of its tails is longer than the other. The three types of skews are shown in Figure 10-3. The first distribution shows a positive skew. This means that it has a long tail in the positive direction. The second distribution has a negative skew since it has a long tail in the negative direction. Finally, the third distribution is symmetric and has no skew.

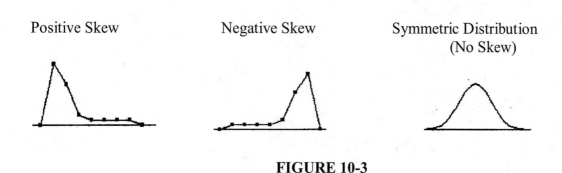

Positive Skew   Negative Skew   Symmetric Distribution (No Skew)

FIGURE 10-3

However, the median ignores many data values and is generally less efficient than the mean, the trimean, and trimmed means.

When there is an odd number of numbers, the median is simply the middle number. For example, the median of 2, 4, and 7 is 4.
When there is an even number of numbers, the median is the mean of the two middle numbers. Thus, the median of the numbers 2, 4, 7, and 12 is $\frac{(4+7)}{2} = 5.5$.

Example 10-3

Find the median of the following beginning salaries of 9 technicians.

$19,160	$20,283	$20,476	$20,537	$21,571
$21,965	$22,419	$22,849	$23,473	

SOLUTION

To find the median salary, count 9/2 ≈5 from either end of the array. The median salary is $21,571 since there are four salaries higher and four salaries lower than it.

four data values below median				median
$19,160	$20,283	$20,476	$20,537	$21,571

four data values above the median

$21,963 $22,419 $22,849 $23,473

Example 10-4

The following numbers represent the age of Mr. Carter's employees:

37   21   41   32   18   40   28   47

Find the median of these data values.

SOLUTION

First arrange the data in ascending.

18 21 28 32   37 40 41 47

The median is the mean of 32 and 37.

$$\text{median} = \frac{(32 + 37)}{2} = \frac{69}{2} = 34.5$$

The median age of these employees is 34.5.

10.2.3 MODE

Mode is the data value that occurs most frequently. It is the only measure of central tendency that can be used with nominal data. That is data in which no ordering of the items is implied. Religious preference, race, and sex are all examples of nominal scales.

The mode is greatly subject to sample fluctuations and should not be used as the only measure of central tendency. Sampling fluctuation refers to the extent to which a statistic takes on different values with different samples. That is, it refers to how much the statistic's value fluctuates from sample to sample. A statistic whose value fluctuates greatly from sample to sample is highly subject to sampling fluctuation.

A further disadvantage of the mode is that many distributions have more than one mode. These distributions are called "multi-modal."

Example 10-5

The following data results from a motion-time study on the time duration of a task:

6   8 10 7 6   11 7 6 12
17 9 8   6 14 11 2 8 10

Find the mode of this data set.

SOLUTION

First form a Frequency Distribution Table.

Data	2	6	7	8	9	10	11	12	14	17
Frequency	1	4	2	3	1	2	2	1	1	1

The mode is 6 because it occurs most frequently.

10.2.4 TRIMEAN

In order to learn how to compute the trimean, you must understand what is meant by the percentile. A percentile rank is the proportion of scores in a distribution that a specific score is greater than or equal to. For instance, if you received a score of 95 on a math test and this score was greater than or equal to the scores of 88% of the students taking the test, then your percentile rank would be 88. You would be in the 88th percentile.

The trimean is computed by adding the 25th percentile plus twice the 50th percentile plus the 75th percentile and dividing by four.

Example 10-6

Suppose that the 25th, 50th, and 75th percentile of a large dataset is 51, 55, and 63 respectively. Compute the trimean.

SOLUTION

$$\text{trimean} = \frac{51 + (2 \times 55) + 63}{4} = 56$$

The trimean is almost as resistant to extreme scores as the median and is less subject to sampling fluctuations than the arithmetic mean in skewed distributions. It is less efficient than the mean for normal distributions. The trimean is a good measure of central tendency and is probably not used as much as it should be.

The efficiency of a statistic is the degree to which the statistic is stable from sample to sample. That is, the less subject to sampling fluctuation a statistic is, the more efficient it is. The efficiency of statistics is measured relative to the efficiency of other statistics and is therefore often called the relative efficiency. If statistic A has a smaller standard error than statistic B, then statistic A is more efficient than statistic B. Standard error is the standard deviation of the sampling distribution of that statistic.

The relative efficiency of two statistics may depend on the distribution involved. For instance, the mean is more efficient than the median for normal distributions but not for many types of skewed distributions.

10.2.5 TRIMMED MEAN

A trimmed mean is calculated by discarding a certain percentage of the lowest and the highest scores and then computing the mean of the remaining scores. For example, a mean trimmed 50% is computed by discarding the lower and higher 25% of the scores and taking the mean of the remaining scores.

The median is the mean trimmed 100% and the arithmetic mean is the mean trimmed 0%.
A trimmed mean is obviously less susceptible to the effects of extreme scores than is the arithmetic mean. It is therefore less susceptible to sampling fluctuation than the mean for skewed distributions. It is less efficient than the mean for normal distributions. Trimmed means are often used in Olympic scoring to minimize the effects of extreme ratings possibly caused by biased judges.

10.3 MEASURES OF DISPERSION

Measures of dispersion indicate the spread of the data values. There are four measures of dispersion. They are range, semi-interquartile range, variance and standard deviation.

10.3.1 RANGE

The range is the simplest measure of spread or dispersion. It is equal to the difference between the largest and the smallest values. The range can be a useful measure of spread because it is so easily understood. However, it is very sensitive to extreme scores since it is based on only two values. The range should almost never be used as the only measure of spread, but can be informative if used as a supplement to other measures of spread such as the standard deviation or semi-interquartile range. The range is a useful statistic to know, but it cannot stand alone as a measure of spread since it takes into account only two scores.

range = highest number – smallest number   (10-4)

Example 10-7

What is the range of the numbers 1, 2, 4, 6,12,15,19, and 26?

SOLUTION

Using equation 10-4,

range = 26 – 1 = 25

Example 10-8

A machine is tooling a part that should be 26 cm long. A machinist randomly selects 8 parts and finds their lengths (in centi-meters) to be as follows:

24.7 cm   26.8 cm   23.2 cm   27.3 cm   25.8 cm   24.9 cm   26.8 cm   26.2 cm

Determine the range of these values.

SOLUTION

From the list of lengths, we determine that the largest value is 27.3 cm and the smallest value is 23.2 cm.

Using equation 10-4,

range = 27.3 cm – 23.2 cm = 4.1 cm

10.3.2 SEMI-INTERQUARTILE RANGE

The semi-interquartile range is computed as one half the difference between the 75th percentile [often called (Q3)] and the 25th percentile (Q1). The formula for semi-interquartile range is therefore: (Q3-Q1)/2.

Since half the scores in a distribution lie between Q3 and Q1, the semi-interquartile range is 1/2 the distance needed to cover 1/2 the scores. In a symmetric distribution, an interval stretching from one semi-interquartile range below the median to one semi-interquartile above the median will contain 1/2 of the scores. This will not be true for a skewed distribution, however.

The semi-interquartile range is little affected by extreme scores, so it is a good measure of spread for skewed distributions. However, it is more subject to sampling fluctuation in normal distributions than is the standard deviation and therefore not often used for data that are approximately normally distributed.

The semi-interquartile range is rarely used as a measure of spread, in part because it is not very mathematically tractable. However, it is influenced less by extreme scores than the standard deviation, is less subject to sampling fluctuations in highly-skewed distributions, and has a good intuitive meaning. It should be used to supplement the standard deviation in most cases.

10.3.3 VARIANCE

The variance is a measure of how spread out a distribution is. It is computed as the average squared deviation of each number from its mean.

In order to fully understand variance we should know the difference between a population and a sample.

A population consists of an entire set of objects, observations, scores or data values that have something in common. For example, a population might be defined as all males between the ages of 15 and 18.

As stated earlier in the chapter, a sample is a subset of a population. Since it is usually impractical to test every member of extremely large population, a sample from the population is typically the best approach available.

The formula for the variance in a population is given by equation 10-5.

$$\sigma^2 = \frac{\sum(x - \mu)^2}{N} \qquad (10\text{-}5)$$

where μ is the mean and N is the number of data values.

The formula for the variance in a sample is given by equation 10-6.

$$s^2 = \frac{\sum(x - M)^2}{N} \qquad (10\text{-}6)$$

where M is the mean of the sample.

s^2 is a biased estimate of σ^2, however.

A statistic is biased if, in the long run, it consistently over or underestimates the parameter it is estimating. More technically it is biased if its expected value is not equal to the parameter. A stopwatch that is a little bit fast gives biased estimates of elapsed time. Bias in this sense is different from the notion of a biased sample. A statistic is positively biased if it tends to overestimate the parameter; a statistic is negatively biased if it tends to underestimate the parameter. An unbiased statistic is not necessarily an accurate statistic. If a statistic is sometimes much too high and sometimes much too low, it can still be unbiased. It would be very imprecise, however. A slightly biased statistic that systematically results in very small overestimates of a parameter could be quite efficient.

Example 10-9

Determine the variance for the numbers 1, 2, and 3 if the mean is 2.

SOLUTION

Using equation 10-5,

$$\sigma^2 = \frac{\sum(x-\mu)^2}{N} = \frac{(1-2)^2 + (2-2)^2 + (3-2)^2}{3} = 0.667$$

By far the most common formula for computing variance in a sample is:

$$s^2 = \frac{\sum(x-M)^2}{N-1}$$

This formula gives an unbiased estimate of σ^2. Since samples are usually used to estimate parameters, s^2 is the most commonly used measure of variance.

10.3.4 STANDARD DEVIATION

The most widely used measure of dispersion is the standard deviation, which is a measure of how much the data relate to the arithmetic mean. In other words, the standard deviation tells you how spread out numbers are from the average.

Although less sensitive to extreme scores than the range, the standard deviation is more sensitive than the semi-interquartile range. Thus, the standard deviation should be supplemented by the semi-interquartile range when the possibility of extreme scores is present.

The standard deviation is by far the most widely used measure of spread. It takes every score into account, has extremely useful properties when used with a normal distribution, and is tractable mathematically and, therefore it appears in many formulas in inferential statistics. The standard deviation is not a good measure of spread in highly-skewed distributions and should be supplemented in those cases by the semi-interquartile range.

Inferential statistics are used to draw inferences about a population from a sample. Consider an experiment in which 10 subjects who performed a task after 24 hours of sleep deprivation scored 12 points lower than 10 subjects who performed after a normal night's sleep. Is the difference real or could it be due to chance? How much larger could the real difference be than the 12 points found in the sample? These are the types of questions answered by inferential statistics.

The standard deviation is the square root of the variance as shown in equation 10-7.

$$\sigma = \sqrt{\sigma^2} \qquad (13\text{-}7)$$

The standard deviation can also be calculated by using equation 10-8.

$$\sigma = \sqrt{\frac{\sum_{i=1}^{n}(x_i - \mu)^2}{N}} \qquad (10\text{-}8)$$

where σ is the standard deviation.

Example 10-10

What is the standard deviation in Example 10-9?

SOLUTION

Using equation 10-7,

$$\sigma = \sqrt{\sigma^2} = \sqrt{0.667} = 0.817$$

Example 10-11

The following values represent the number of defective diodes in lots of 100:

1   6   5   2   9   6   4   8   7   5

Find the standard deviation of the data values.

SOLUTION

First find the mean, using equation 10-2.

$$\mu = \frac{\sum x_i}{N} = \frac{(1+6+5+2+9+6+4+8+7+5)}{10} = 5.3$$

Second, we calculate the difference between the mean and the data values as shown in the second column of Table 10-2. Third, we square each entry in the second column and place the result in the third column of Table 10-2.

TABLE 10-2

x	$x-\mu$	$(x-\mu)^2$
1	-4.3	18.49
6	0.7	0.49
5	-0.3	0.09
2	-3.3	10.89
9	3.7	13.69
6	0.7	0.49
4	-1.3	1.69
8	2.7	7.29
7	1.7	2.89
5	-0.3	0.09
Σ 53 (Total Sum)		Σ 56.1 (Total Sum)

Using equation 10-8 to compute the standard deviation,

$$\sigma = \sqrt{\frac{\sum_{i=1}^{n}(x_i - \mu)^2}{N}} = \sqrt{\frac{56.1}{10}} = \sqrt{5.61} \approx 2.4$$

To calculate the standard deviation from grouped data, use can use equation 10-9.

$$\sigma = \sqrt{\frac{\sum_{i=1}^{n} f_i \times (x_i - \mu)^2}{\sum_{i=1}^{n} f_i}} \qquad (10-9)$$

f_i = frequency of data value x_i.

To calculate the mean from grouped data, use equation 10-10.

$$\mu = \frac{\sum\limits_{i=1}^{n} f \times x}{\sum\limits_{i=1}^{n} f_i} \qquad\qquad (10\text{-}10)$$

Example 10-12

Professor Jones gave back the math test to her students. Four students earned the grade of 70. Six students received a 73. Three students made the grade of 78. Five students earned the grade of 80. Seven students made an 88. Using the frequency distribution, find the average score on the test and standard deviation.

SOLUTION

The first two columns in Table 10-3 show the test scores for Professor Jones's mathematics class.

First fill in the ($f \times x$) column, by multiplying the first and second columns.

Second calculate the mean using equation 10-10.

$$\mu = \frac{\sum\limits_{i=1}^{n} f \times x}{\sum\limits_{i=1}^{n} f_i} = \frac{280 + 438 + 234 + 400 + 616}{25} = \frac{1968}{25} = 78.72$$

The average score on the test was 78.72.

TABLE 10-3

x	f	$f \times x$	$x\text{-}\mu$	$(x\text{-}\mu)^2$	$f \times (x\text{-}\mu)^2$
70	4	280	-8.72	76.04	304.16
73	6	438	-5.72	32.72	196.32
78	3	234	-0.72	0.52	1.56
80	5	400	1.28	1.64	8.20
88	7	616	9.28	86.12	602.84
	Σ 25	Σ 1968			Σ 1113.08

Next fill in the remainder of the table.

Compute the standard deviation using equation 10-9.

$$\sigma = \sqrt{\frac{\sum_{i=1}^{n} f_i \times (x_i - \mu)^2}{\sum_{i=1}^{n} f_i}} = \sqrt{\frac{304.16 + 196.32 + 1.56 + 8.20 + 602.84}{4 + 6 + 3 + 5 + 7}} = \sqrt{\frac{1113.08}{25}} = 6.67$$

The standard deviation is 6.67 points.

Equation 10-11 is an alternate formula for computing the standard deviation.

$$\sigma = \sqrt{\frac{\sum_{i=1}^{n} (x_i)^2}{N} - \left(\frac{\sum_{i=1}^{n} (x_i)}{N}\right)^2} \qquad (10\text{-}11)$$

The first term is the mean of the squares. The second term is the square of the mean.

Example 10-13

The following measurements (in milli-meters) represent the variation of metal part from its specified length:

1.83 mm   4.31 mm   3.42 mm   4.08 mm   2.67 mm   3.95 mm

Find the standard deviation using the alternate formula for computing the standard deviation.

SOLUTION

First calculate the square of each data value x_i^2 and place the results in the second column of Table 10-4.

There are six measurements so N is equal to 6.

TABLE 10-4

x_i	x_i^2
1.83	3.349
4.31	18.576
3.42	11.696
4.08	16.65
2.67	7.129
3.95	15.61
Σ 20.26	Σ 73.01

Using equation 10-11,

$$\sigma = \sqrt{\frac{\sum_{i=1}^{n}(x_i)^2}{N} - \left(\frac{\sum_{i=1}^{n}(x_i)}{N}\right)^2} = \sqrt{\frac{73.01}{6} - \left(\frac{20.26}{6}\right)^2} = \sqrt{12.168 - 11.402} = \sqrt{0.766} = 0.875 \text{ mm}$$

10.3.5 SIGNIFICANCE OF STANDARD DEVIATION

If we take enough experimental measurements, the curve of the data set usually approaches a normal, bell-shaped distribution as shown in Figure 10-4. Notice that for the normal distribution, approximately 68% of the measurements fall within one standard deviation of the mean, or $\bar{x} - s$ and $\bar{x} + s$. The symbol s will represent the standard deviation. The symbol $\bar{x}$ will represent the mean. Also, roughly 95% of the measurements fall within the two standard deviations of the mean, or within $\bar{x} - 2s$ and $\bar{x} + 2s$. Almost 99.7% of the measurements fall within the three standard deviations of the mean, or within $\bar{x} - 3s$ and $\bar{x} + 3s$.

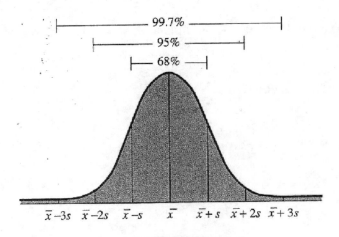

FIGURE 10-4

Example 10-14

For the data set of Example 10-12, calculate the interval of values within one standard deviation of the mean. Compare this result with the actual percentage of the data set that falls within this range.

SOLUTION

To find the interval of values within one standard deviation of the mean, we calculate $\bar{x} - s$ and $\bar{x} + s$. From the calculations in Example 10-14, $\bar{x} = \mu = 78.72$ and $s = \sigma = 6.67$.

$\bar{x} - s = 78.72 - 6.67 = 72.05$
$\bar{x} + s = 78.72 + 6.67 = 85.39$

The interval of values within one standard deviation of the mean is 72.05 to 85.39. From the data set itself, we find that 14 of the 25 values, or 56%, fall within this interval.

Example 10-15

For the data set of Example 10-12, calculate the interval of values within two standard deviation of the mean. Compare this result with the actual percentage of the data set that falls within that range.

SOLUTION

$\bar{x} - 2s = 78.72 - (2 \times 6.67) = 78.72 - 13.34 = 65.38$
$\bar{x} + 2s = 78.72 + (2 \times 6.67) = 78.72 + 13.34 = 92.06$

The interval of values within two standard deviations of the mean is 65.38 to 92.06. From the data set itself, we find that all of the 25 values, or 100 %, fall within this interval.

If the mean and standard deviation of a normal distribution are known, it is relatively easy to figure out the percentile rank of a person obtaining a specific score. To be more concrete, assume a test in Introductory Psychology is normally distributed with a mean of 80 and a standard deviation of 5. What is the percentile rank of a person who received a score of 70 on the test? Mathematical statisticians have developed ways of determining the proportion of a distribution that is below a given number of standard deviations from the mean. They have shown that only 2.3 % of the population will be less than or equal to a score two standard deviations below the mean. In terms of the Introductory Psychology test example, this means that a person scoring 70 would be in the 2.3 percentile, as shown in Figure 10.5.

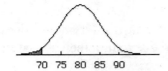

FIGURE 10-5

The graph in Figure 10-5 also shows the distribution of scores on the test. The shaded area is 2.3% of the total area. The proportion of the area below 70 is equal to the proportion of the scores below 70.

10.3.6 Z-SCORES

When a score is expressed in standard deviation units, it is referred to as a Z-score. A score that is one standard deviation above the mean has a Z-score of 1. A score that is one standard deviation below the mean has a Z-score of -1. A score that is at the mean would have a Z-score of 0. The normal curve with Z-scores along the abscissa looks exactly like the normal curve with standard deviation units along the abscissa.

Why are 70 considered two standard deviations below the mean in Example 10-12? The mean is 80 and the standard deviation is 5. Since 70 is 10 points below the mean (80-70 = 10) and since a standard deviation is 5 points, there is a distance of 2 standard deviations between the 80 and 70 (10/5 = 2). In general, the number of standard deviations a score is from the mean can be computed by using equation 10-12.

$$z = \frac{x - \mu}{\sigma} \qquad (10\text{-}12)$$

where z is the number of standard deviations above the mean (μ) the score x is. The standard deviation is (σ). When z is negative it means that x is below the mean. Using equation 10-12 for this illustration,

$$z = \frac{70 - 80}{5} = -2$$

As stated earlier, only 2.3% of the population scores below a score two standard deviations below the mean.

10.3.7 PERCENTILE RANKS

Another useful derived score is the percentile rank. The percentile rank is the percentage or proportion of scores that score lower than a given score. If you received a percentile rank of 90 then 90% of the scores would be lower than your score and 10% of the scores would be higher. You could also say that your score is at the 90th percentile. The median for any set of scores (by definition) is at the 50th percentile. That is, 50% of the scores are lower than the median, and 50% of the scores are higher than the median. Ordinarily percentiles are reported as whole numbers so the highest percentile possible would be 99 and the lowest possible would be 1. A score that is one standard deviation below the mean would have a percentile rank of 16 (0.13 + 2.14 + 13.59 = 15.86). A score that is two standard deviations below the mean would have a percentile rank of 2 (0.13 + 2.14 = 2.27). A score that was three standard deviations below the mean would be at the 1st percentile and one that was three standard deviations above the mean would be at the 99th percentile. Some test designers have used the concept of extended percentile ranks to make finer divisions for scores at the upper half of the 99th percentile and at the lower half of the 1st percentile.

What about a person scoring 75 on the test in Example 10-12? The proportion of the area below 75 is the same as the proportion of scores below 75, as shown in Figure 10-6.

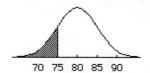

FIGURE 10-6

A score of 75 is one standard deviation below the mean because the mean is 80 and the standard deviation is 5. Mathematical statisticians have determined that 15.9% of the scores in a normal distribution are lower than a score one standard deviation below the mean. Therefore, the proportion of the scores below 75 is 0.159 and a person scoring 75 would have a percentile rank score of 15.9.

Table 10-5 gives the proportion of the scores below various values of z. z is computed with the formula: $z = \dfrac{x - \mu}{\sigma}$. Table 10-5 is called the z-table.

TABLE 10-5

z	Area from -∞ to z
-3.0	0.0013
-2.5	0.0062
-2.0	0.0227
-1.5	0.0668
-1.0	0.1587
-0.5	0.3085
0.0	0.500
0.5	0.06915
1.0	0.8413
1.5	0.9332
2.0	0.9772
2.5	0.9938
3.0	0.9987

When z is negative it means that x is below the mean. Thus, a z of -2 means that x is -2 standard deviations above the mean. This is the same thing as being +2 standard deviations below the mean. What is the percentile rank of a person receiving a score of 90 on the test?

The graph in Figure 10-7 shows that most people scored below 90. Since 90 is 2 standard deviations above the mean [z = (90 - 80)/5 = 2] it can be determined from Table 10-5 that a z score of 2 is equivalent to the 97.7th percentile: The proportion of people scoring below 90 is thus .977.

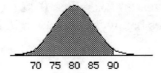

70 75 80 85 90

FIGURE 10-7

What score on the Introductory Psychology test would it have taken to be in the 75th percentile?

(Remember the test has a mean of 80 and a standard deviation of 5.) The answer is computed by reversing the steps in the previous discussion. First, determine how many standard deviations above the mean it takes to be in the 75th percentile. This can be found by using a more detailed z-table and finding the z associated with 0.75. The value of z is 0.674. Thus, one must be 0.674 standard deviations above the mean to be in the 75th percentile. Since the standard deviation is 5, one must be $[(5) \times (0.674)]$ = 3.37 points above the mean. Since the mean is 80, a score of 80 + 3.37 = 83.37 is necessary. Rounding off, a score of 83 is needed to be in the 75th percentile, as shown in Figure 13-8. Since, $z = \dfrac{x - \mu}{\sigma}$ a little algebra demonstrates that $x = \{\mu + (z \times \sigma)\}$. For the present discussion, $x = 80 + [(0.674) \times (5)] = 83.37$ as just shown.

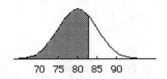

70 75 80 85 90

FIGURE 10-8

10.3.8 T-SCORES

Another commonly used derived scores based on the normal curve, is the T-score. T-scores are derived scores with a mean of 50 and a standard deviation of 10. The average T-score for a group of scorers would be 50. We can see that a T-score of 60 would be equivalent to a Z-score of 1, and a Deviation IQ score of 115. Each of these scores would be one standard deviation above the mean and would be equal to or higher than 84.13% of the scores (50.00% + 34.13% = 84.13%).

10.4 GRADE POINT AVERAGE (GPA)

4 – Point System A = 4.0, A- = 3.7, B+ = 3.3, B = 3.0, B- = 2.7, C+ = 2.3, C = 2.0, C- = 1.7, D+ = 1.3, D = 1.0 and F = 0.0

Equation 13-13 is used to compute the GPA.

$$GPA = \frac{\Sigma \text{ grade points}}{n \text{ (credits)}} \qquad (10\text{-}13)$$

Example 10-16

Gertrude's Report Card

Course Credit	Course Letter Grade
4	A
2	C
6	A
3	B

What is Gertrude's GPA?

SOLUTION

Calculated Grade Points (Σ grade points)

$4 \times 4 = 16$
$2 \times 2 = 4$
$6 \times 4 = 24$
$3 \times 3 = 9$

Using equation 13-13,

$$GPA = \frac{(16 + 4 + 24 + 9)}{15} = 3.533$$

Example 10-17

Below is Dora's grade distribution and recorded scores from her Math class. What is Dora's grade (weighted average)?

Sample Grade Distribution Chart

HW	10% [Drop the lowest]
Test #1	20%
Test #2	20%
Quiz	30% [Drop the lowest]
Lab Reports	15%
Project	5%

HW:	100	80	75	95	100	90	60	80	85	0
Quiz:	90	50	80	100	100	100	0	25
Lab Reports:	100	100	100	100	90	95	90	100	100	70
Test #1:	85
Test#2:	75
Project:	100

SOLUTION

$$\text{HW Average} = \frac{100 + 80 + 75 + 95 + 100 + 90 + 60 + 80 + 85}{9} = \frac{765}{9} = 85$$

$$\text{HW Weight} = 85 \times 0.1 = 8.5$$

$$\text{Quiz Average} = \frac{90 + 50 + 80 + 100 + 100 + 25}{7} = \frac{545}{7} = 77.86$$

$$\text{Quiz Weight} = 77.86 \times 0.30 = 23.36$$

$$\text{Lab Report Average} = \frac{100 + 100 + 100 + 100 + 90 + 95 + 90 + 100 + 100 + 70}{10} = \frac{945}{10} = 94.5$$

$$\text{Lab Report Weight} = 94.5 \times 0.15 = 14.2$$

$$\text{Test \#1 Weight} = 85 \times 0.20 = 17$$

$$\text{Test \#2 Weight} = 75 \times 0.20 = 15$$

$$\text{Project Weight} = 100 \times 0.05 = 5$$

Add all the weights.

Total Weight $= 8.5 + 23.36 + 14.2 + 17 + 15 + 5 = 83.06$.

The final grade is an 83.

10.5 FREQUENCY DISTRIBUTION

Frequency tables and pictures are two major methods of summarizing a set of numbers. Each method has advantages and disadvantages. The use of one method need not exclude the use of the other. A frequency table is a way of organizing the data by listing every possible score (including those not actually obtained in the sample) as a column of numbers and the frequency of occurrence of each score as another. Pictures can be displayed statistically as histograms, bar graphs and polygons.

10.6 FREQUENCY TABLES

Computing the frequency of a score is simply a matter of counting the number of times that score appears in the set of data. This simple tabulation has two drawbacks. When a variable can take continuous values instead of discrete values or when the number of possible values is too large, the table construction becomes cumbersome. Also, it is necessary to include scores with zero frequency if you want to represent the data as a histogram, or frequency polygon later.

Example 10-18

The following data reveal the number of kids who met Santa Claus at the Mall of America during 15-minute intervals for 4 hours.

12	15	9	7
12	8	10	12
9	10	7	11
8	12	6	13

Construct a frequency distribution table for the data.

SOLUTION

To construct a frequency distribution, we arrange the data in ascending order and tabulate the number of times each event occurs. The frequency distribution for the data is given in Table 10-6.

TABLE 10-6

Number of kids visiting Santa Claus	5	6	7	8	9	10	11	12	13
Frequency	0	1	2	2	2	2	1	4	1

When data contain a large number of observations with a wide range of scores, it is wise to organize the information into equal intervals. None of the interval should overlap. A score should belong to only one interval. Generally, we should build between 5 and 12 intervals. In order to determine the width of the interval, subtract the smallest score from the largest score and divide the result by the number of intervals.

Example 10-19

Oprah did a research project in which she was interested in the amount of quarters that were deposited in the Salvation Army's cup. She randomly selected groups of 100 people who denoted quarters in the cup.

30	35	12	60	21	19	5	8	25	15	52
53	33	22	57	59	5	12	15	39	44	41
52	55	27	17	9	42	52	55	34	21	56

Construct a frequency distribution table for the data.

SOLUTION

First, we divide the range of values into 9 intervals. The approximate width of each interval is $\frac{(60-5)}{9} \approx 6$. Then we determine the frequency distribution of each interval.

This information is summarized in Table 10-7.

TABLE 10-7

Interval	0-6	7-12	13-18	19-24	25-30	31-36	37-42	43-48	49-54	55-60
Frequency	2	4	3	4	3	2	2	1	4	6

10.7 GRAPHING FREQUENCY DISTRIBUTION

The information contained in the frequency table may be transformed to a graphical or pictorial form. No information is gained or lost in this transformation, but the human information processing system often finds the graphical or pictorial presentation easier to comprehend. There are two major means of drawing a graph, histograms and frequency polygons. The choice of method is often a matter of convention, although there are times when one or the other is clearly the appropriate choice.

10.8 HISTOGRAMS

A histogram is drawn by plotting the scores (midpoints) on the *x-axis* and the frequencies on the *y-axis*. A bar is drawn for each score value, the width of the bar corresponding to the real limits of the interval and the height corresponding to the frequency of the occurrence of the score value. When the data may be assumed to be interval, then the histogram can sometimes have a large number of lines, called data ink, which make the comprehension of the graph difficult. A frequency polygon is often preferred in these cases because much less ink is needed to present the same amount of information.

Example 10-20

The following grades were recorded for a Midterm exam in CST 120:

92	97	77	72	90	80	44	87	60	61	95
72	40	83	90	87	65	46	96	82	95	80
70	35	70	85	68	95	32	97	85	80	37
79	73	63	80	85						

Draw a histogram to depict the distribution of the grades.

SOLUTION

First, we will divide the grades into equal intervals. The approximate interval width for seven intervals is $\frac{(97-32)}{7} \approx 9$. Frequency of grades during the intervals is given in Table 10-8.

TABLE 10-8

Interval	30-39	40-49	50-59	60-69	70-79	80-89	90-100
Frequency	3	3	0	5	7	10	8

Next, we construct a histogram using rectangles whose width represents the length of the data interval and whose height represents the frequency of that interval. In the case of grouped data, generally the horizontal axis is labeled with the midpoint of the interval. Remember that the midpoint of the interval is half the difference in interval endpoints. The histogram is shown in Figure 10-9.

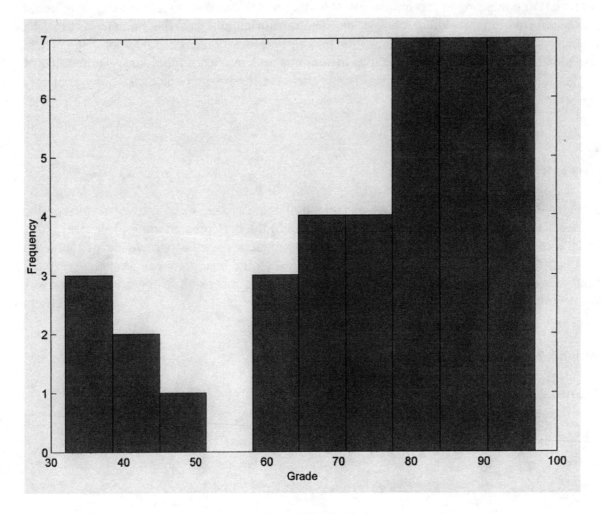

FIGURE 10-9

10.9 FREQUENCY POLYGON

A frequency polygon is a broken-line graphically display of a frequency table. The intervals are shown on the *x-axis* and the number of scores in each interval (frequency of occurrence) is represented on the *y-axis*. The frequency of occurrence is represented by the height of a point located above the middle of the interval. The points are connected so that together with the x-axis they form a polygon. Frequency polygons are useful for comparing distributions, too.

Example 10-21

Draw a frequency polygon for the data given in Example 10-20.

SOLUTION

242

You can construct a frequency polygon from a histogram by joining the midpoints of the tops of the rectangles with line segments. That is, we must place a point above the data group at the appropriate frequency. We will connect successive points with straight line segments. Since polygons are closed figures, we must add two additional intervals. See Table 10-9 below.

TABLE 10-9

Interval	20-29	30-39	40-49	50-59	60-69	70-79	80-89	90-99	100-105
Frequency	0	3	3	0	5	7	10	8	0
Midpoint	24.5	34.5	44.5	54.5	64.5	74.5	84.5	94.5	104.5

We will calculate the leftmost midpoint and the rightmost midpoint. The leftmost interval is 20 - 29 with a midpoint of $\frac{20+29}{2} = 24.5$. The rightmost interval is 100 – 105 with a midpoint of $\frac{100+105}{2} = 104.5$. All the other midpoints are calculated in a similar fashion. The frequency polygon is shown in Figure 10-10. This graph can be created using Microsoft Excel or a similar software tool.

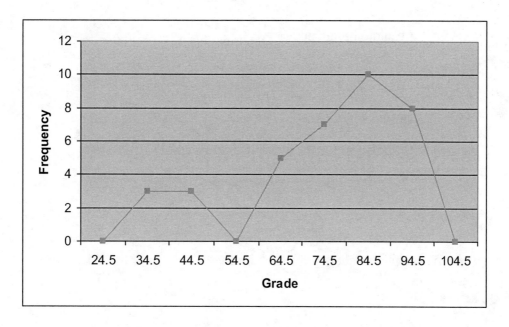

FIGURE 10-10

10.10 ABSOLUTE FREQUENCY POLYGON

The frequency polygon is sometimes called the *absolute frequency polygon*. An absolute frequency polygon is drawn exactly like a histogram except that points are drawn rather than bars. The *x-axis* begins with the midpoint of the interval immediately lower than the lowest interval, and ends with the interval immediately higher than the highest interval. In the example, this would mean that the score values of 24.5 and 104.5 would appear on the *x-axis* as shown in Table 10-9. The frequency polygon is drawn by plotting a point on the graph at the intersection of the midpoint of the interval and the height of the frequency. When the points are plotted, the dots are connected with lines, resulting in a frequency polygon.

No student scored in the range of 50 – 59. Note that the frequency for this score is zero, and the line goes down to the *x-axis*. Failing to go down to the X-axis when the frequency is zero is the most common error students make in drawing non-cumulative frequency polygons.

10.11 RELATIVE FREQUENCY POLYGON

In order to draw a relative frequency polygon, the relative frequency of each score interval must first be calculated and placed in the appropriate column in the frequency table. The relative frequency of a score is another name for the proportion of scores that have a particular value. The relative frequency is computed by dividing the frequency of a score by the number of scores (N).

Equation 10-14 is used for determining the relative frequency.

$$\text{Relative Frequency} = \frac{\text{Absolute Frequency}}{N} \qquad (10\text{-}14)$$

Example 10-22

Draw a relative frequency polygon for the data given in Example 10-20.

SOLUTION

We will compute the relative frequency for each interval.

We have 38 scores so $N = 38$.

Using equation 10-14,

$$\text{For interval 20 -29: Relative Frequency} = \frac{\text{Absolute Frequency}}{N} = \frac{0}{38} = 0$$

$$\text{For interval 30 -39: Relative Frequency} = \frac{\text{Absolute Frequency}}{N} = \frac{3}{38} = 0.079$$

For interval 40 - 49: Relative Frequency = $\dfrac{\text{Absolute Frequency}}{N} = \dfrac{3}{38} = 0.079$

For interval 50 -59: Relative Frequency = $\dfrac{\text{Absolute Frequency}}{N} = \dfrac{0}{38} = 0$

For interval 60 -69: Relative Frequency = $\dfrac{\text{Absolute Frequency}}{N} = \dfrac{5}{38} = 0.132$

For interval 70 -79: Relative Frequency = $\dfrac{\text{Absolute Frequency}}{N} = \dfrac{7}{38} = 0.184$

For interval 80 -89: Relative Frequency = $\dfrac{\text{Absolute Frequency}}{N} = \dfrac{10}{38} = 0.263$

For interval 90 -100: Relative Frequency = $\dfrac{\text{Absolute Frequency}}{N} = \dfrac{8}{24} = 0.210$

For interval 100 -105: Relative Frequency = $\dfrac{\text{Absolute Frequency}}{N} = \dfrac{0}{38} = 0$

The modified frequency table is given Table 10-10.

TABLE 10-10

Interval	20-29	30-39	40-49	50-59	60-69	70-79	80-89	90-99	100-105
Absolute Frequency	0	3	3	0	5	7	10	8	0
Midpoint	24.5	34.5	44.5	54.5	64.5	74.5	84.5	94.5	104.5
Relative Frequency	0	0.079	0.079	0	0.132	0.184	0.263	0.210	0

The relative frequency polygon is shown in Figure 10-11.

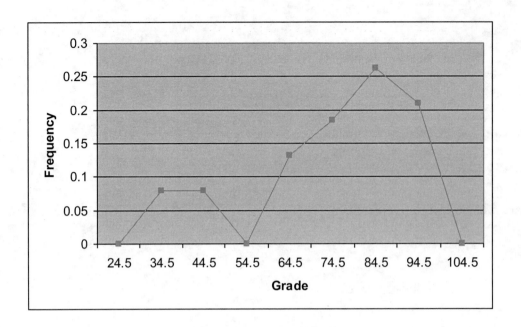

FIGURE 10-11

The relative frequency polygon is drawn exactly like the absolute frequency polygon except the *y-axis* is labeled and incremented with relative frequency rather than absolute frequency. A relative frequency may be transformed into an absolute frequency by using an opposite transformation; that is, multiplying by the number of scores (N). For this reason the size of the sample on which the relative frequency is based is usually presented somewhere on the graph. Generally speaking, relative frequency is more useful than absolute frequency, because the size of the sample has been taken into account.

10.12 USING MATLAB FOR TECHNICAL STATISTICS

Because of its array orientation, MATLAB readily performs statistical analyses on data sets. While MATLAB by the default considers data sets stored in column-oriented arrays, data analysis can be conducted along any specified dimension. That is, unless specified otherwise, each column of an array represents a different variable and each row represents individual samples or observations.

By default, data analysis in MATLAB is performed on column-oriented matrices. Different variables are stored in individual columns, and each row represents a different observation of each variable. Many data analysis functions work along any dimension, provided it is specified as the last input arguments.

10.12.1 CALCULATING THE MEAN

For vectors, mean (x) is the mean value of the elements in x. For matrices, mean (x) is a row vector containing the mean value of each column. For N-D arrays, mean (x) is the mean value of the elements along the first non-singleton dimension of x. mean (x,dim), takes the mean along the dimension (dim) of x.

10.12.2 CALCULATING THE STANDARD DEVIATION

For vectors, std (x) returns the standard deviation. For matrices, std (x) is a row vector containing the standard deviation of each column. For N-D arrays, std (x) is the standard deviation of the elements along the first non-singleton dimension of x.

std (x) normalizes by (N-1) where N is the sequence length. This makes squaring the standard deviation [std ((x)^ 2)] the best unbiased estimate of the variance if x is a sample from a normal distribution.

std (x,1) normalizes By N and produces the second moment of the sample about its mean. Std (x,0) is the same as std (x).

std (x, flag, dim) takes the standard deviation along the dimension (dim) of x. When flag = 0 STD normalizes (N-1), otherwise std normalizes by N.

10.12.3 CALCULATING THE VARIANCE

For vectors, var (x) returns the variance of x. For matrices, var (x) is a row vector containing the variance of each column of x.

Var (x) normalizes by N -1 where N is the sequence length. This makes var (x) the best unbiased estimate of the variance if x is a sample from a normal distribution.

var (x,1) normalizes by N and produces the second moment of the sample about its mean.

var (x,W) computes the variance using the weight vector, W. The number of elements in

W must equal the number of rows in x unless W is equal to one which is treated as a short-cut for a vector of ones.

The elements of W must be positive. var normalizes W by dividing each element in W by the sum of all its elements.

The variance is the square of the standard deviation (std).

Example 10-23

Use MATLAB to find the mean, standard deviation and variance of the following maximum summer temperatures recorded for city called Metropolis over the past five years.

Average Temperatures: 82°F 75°F 78°F   84°F 77°F

SOLUTION

\>> temp = [82 75 78 84 77];

Press <u>enter</u> on the keyboard.

This line command creates an array called temp and stores the five temperature data points into it.

First, MATLAB will be used to calculate the mean or average value of the summer temperatures.

\>> mean (temp)

Press <u>enter</u> on the keyboard.

MATLAB will display:

ans

=

79.2

Second, MATLAB will be used to calculate the standard deviation of the summer temperatures.

\>> std (temp)

Press <u>enter</u> on the keyboard.

MATLAB will display:

ans

=

3.7014

Third, MATLAB will be used to calculate the variance of the summer temperatures.

>> var (temp)

Press enter on the keyboard.

MATLAB will display:

ans

$=$

   13.7

10.13 CREATING HISTOGRAMS USING MATLAB

There are four common types of histograms that can be created in MATLAB. The formatting for these is described below:

1. N = HIST (Y) biases the elements of Y into equally spaced containers and returns the number of elements in each container. If Y is a matrix, HIST works down columns.

2. N = HIST(Y,M), where M is a scalar, using M bias.

3. N = HIST (Y,X) where X is a vector. This histogram returns the distribution of Y among bins with centers specified by X.

4. [N,X] = HIST (…) also returns the position of the bin centers in X.

Example 10-24

The following grades were recorded from the third test in SOT 120:

99	91	91	58	97	72	0	81	32	25
32	91	84	94	14	49	55	31	101	23
50	7	0	73	77	84	66	52	30	95
64	27	73	50	55	68	93			

Use MATLAB to create a histogram for the distribution of the grades.

SOLUTION

>> N = [99,91,91,58,97,72,0,81,32,25,32,91,84,94,14,49,55,31,101,23,50,7,0,73,77,84,
       66,52,30,95,64,27,73,50,55,68,93];

Press enter on the keyboard.

This line command creates an array called N and stores the 37 data scores into it.

MATLAB is now ready to generate the histogram.

>> hist (N)

Press enter on the keyboard.

>> xlabel ('Grades')

Press enter on the keyboard.

>> ylabel ('Frequency')

Press enter on the keyboard.

The histogram is shown in Figure 10-12.

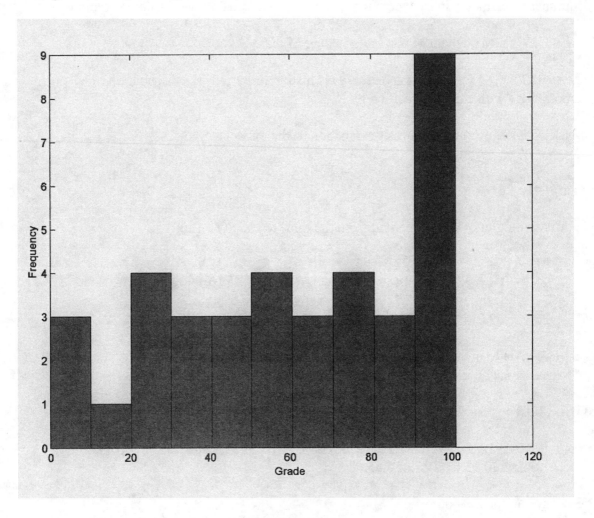

FIGURE 10-12

10.14 USING MATLAB FOR CURVE FITTING

In many applications, there is a challenge of fitting a curve to measured data. Sometimes the chosen curve passes through the data points, but at other times the curve comes close to, but does not pass through the data points. In most cases, the curve is chosen so that the sum of the squared errors at the data points is minimized. This is called a *least squares* curve fit. Least squares can be done using any set of basis functions. MATHLAB will use a polynomial in this case because it is more straightforward and can be approximated as a truncated power series. In MATHLAB the function *polyfit* solves the least square polynomial curve-fitting problem.

To use *polyfit*, we must give it the above data and the order or degree of the polynomial we wish to best fit to the data. If we choose n = 1 as the order, the best straight-line approximation will be found. This is often called *linear regression*. On the other hand, if we choose n = 2 as the order, a *quadratic polynomial* will be found.

The POLYFIT function fits the polynomial to data.

POLYFIT (X,Y,N) finds the coefficients of a polynomial P(X) of degree N that fits the data. P(X(I))˜= Y(I) in a least-squares sense.

[P,S] = POLYFIT (X,Y,N) returns the polynomial coefficients P and a structure S for use with POLYVAL. This function will produce error bounds which contain at least 50% of the predictions.

POLYVAL will evaluate the polynomial.

Y = POLYVAL (P,X), where P is a vector of length N + 1. The elements of P are the coefficients of a polynomial. Y is the value of the polynomial evaluated at X.

Y = P(1)*X^N + P(2)*X^(N − 1) +...+ P(N)*X + P(N + 1)

If X is a matrix or vector, the polynomial is evaluated at all points in X.

[Y,DELTA] = POLYVAL(P,X,S) uses the optional output structure generated by POLYFIT to generate error estimates, Y +/- delta. If the errors in the data input to POLYFIT are independent normal with constant variance, Y +/- DELTA contains at least 50% of the predictions.

POLYVALM evaluates polynomials with a matrix argument. POLYVALM (V,X) where V is a vector whose elements are the coefficients of a polynomial evaluated with matrix argument X. X must be a square matrix.

Example 10-25

The following grades were recorded from the first electric circuits test in SOT 211:

49	70	48	85	84	57
63	90	80	90	76	78

Use MATLAB to create a curve to fit the grade distribution of the first electric circuits test.

a) Use a first-order approximation (straight-line or linear regression).

b) Use a second-order approximation (quadratic approximation).

SOLUTION

Figure 10-13 shows the raw data.

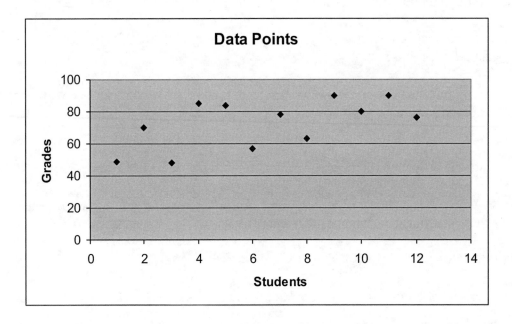

FIGURE 10-13

a) There are twelve students in the course so we will store that count in an array called *x*.

>> x = [1,2,3,4,5,6,7,8,9,10,11,12];

Press <u>enter</u> on the keyboard.

We will store the twelve grades in an array called *y*.

>> y = [49,70,48,85,84,57,78,63,90,80,90,76];

Press <u>enter</u> on the keyboard.

Since this is a straight-line approximation, we choose n = 1.

>> n = 1;

Now MATLAB will use its curve-fitting function *polyfit* to perform a straight-line approximation.

>> p = polyfit(x,y,n)

MATLAB will display:

p =

   2.3916   56.9545

The output of polyfit is a row vector of the polynomial coefficients.

Here the solution is:

$y(x) = 2.3916x + 56.9545$

MATLAB will use the *polyval* function to generate error estimates for plotting.

>> xi = 1:1:12;

>> yi = polyval(p,xi);

>> plot (x,y,'-o',xi,yi,'--')

>> xlabel('students'), ylabel('$y = f(x)$')

Title ('First Order Curve Fitting')

The first order curve-fitting solution is shown in Figure 10-14.

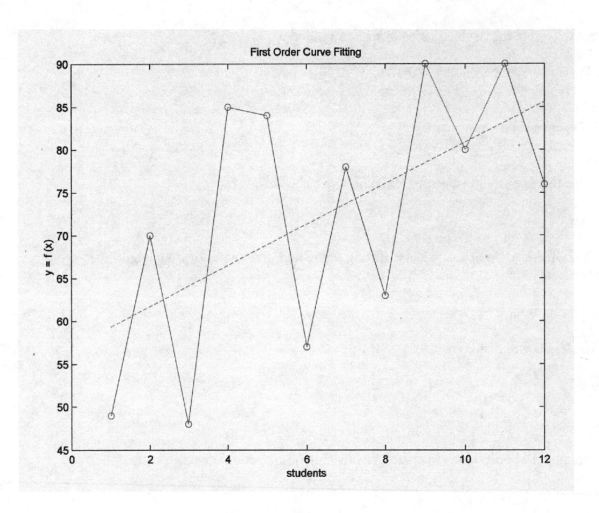

FIGURE 10-14

b) Since this is a quadratic approximation, we choose n = 2.

>> n = 2;

Now MATLAB will use its curve-fitting function *polyfit* to perform a quadratic approximation.

>> p = polyfit(x,y,n)

MATLAB will display:

p =

  -0.2398   5.5085   49.6818

The output of polyfit is a row vector of the polynomial coefficients.

Here the solution is:

$y(x) = -0.2398x^2 + 5.5085x + 49.6818$

MATLAB will use the *polyval* function to generate error estimates for plotting.

\>> xi = 1:1:12;

\>> yi = polyval(p,xi);

\>> plot (x,y,'-o',xi,yi,'--')

\>> xlabel('students'), ylabel('$y = f(x)$')

\>> title ('Second Order Curve Fitting')

The second order curve-fitting solution is shown in Figure 10-15.

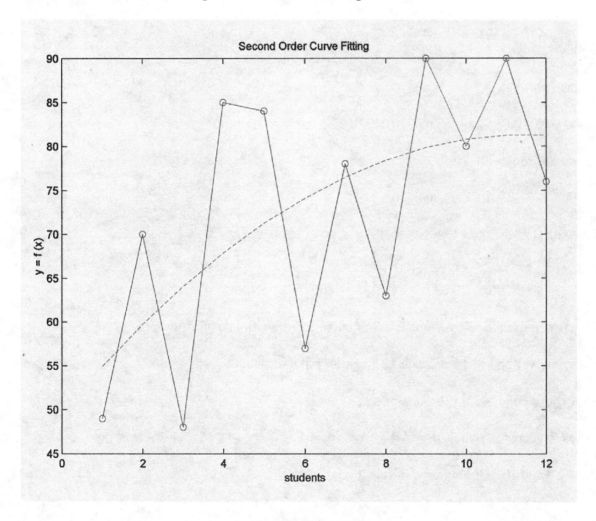

FIGURE 10-15

The quadratic approximation in Figure 10-15 is a better curve fit than the straight-line approximation in Figure 10-14, because it fits more of the data points.

Example 10-26

Use MATLAB to create a graph that shows the 2nd order and the 10th order curve fitting of Example 13-25.

SOLUTION

MATLAB will use its curve-fitting function *polyfit* to create a 10th order polynomial.

>> pp = polyfit(x,y,10) % display polynomial coefficients as a column

pp =

  1.0e+004 *

  Columns 1 through 7

  -0.0000   0.0000 -0.0001   0.0010 -0.0109   0.0747 -0.3356

  Columns 8 through 11

   0.9705 -1.7047   1.6127 -0.6028

Here the solution is:

$$y(x) = 1 \times 10^4[-0x^{10} + 0x^9 - 0x^8 + 0.0010x^7 - 0.0109x^6 + 0.0747x^5 - 0.3356x^4$$
$$+ 0.9705x^3 - 1.7047x^2 + 1.6127x - 0.6028]$$

MATLAB will use the *polyval* function to generate error estimates for plotting.

>> y10 = polyval(pp,xi); % evaluate 10th – order polynomial

>> plot (x,y,'-o',xi,yi,'--',xi,y10) % plot data

>> xlabel('students'), ylabel('$y = f(x)$')

>> title ('2nd and 10th Order Curve Fitting')

The second order curve-fitting solution is shown in Figure 10-16.

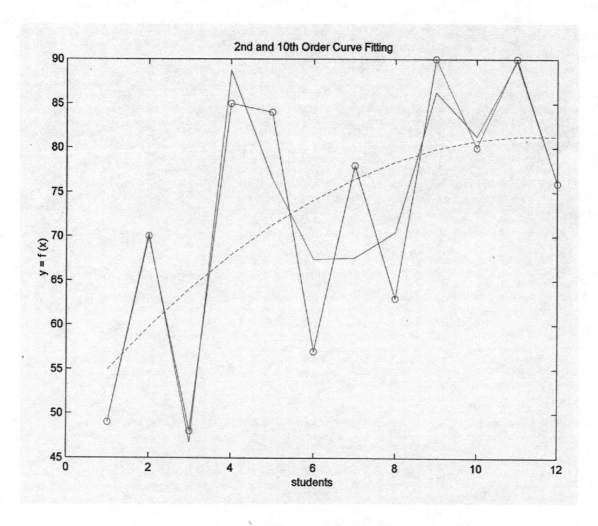

FIGURE 10-16

The red curve is the 10th order curve fitting. The 10th order curve fits the data points better than the 2nd order curve (quadratic approximation).

Appendices

HOMEWORK FOR CHAPTER 7

1. Convert the following numbers to scientific notation:

   a) 123
   b) 4,500
   c) 750,000
   d) 1,250,000
   e) 0.25
   f) 0.0056
   g) 0.0000002

2. Convert the following scientific notations to normal (conventional) numbers:

   a) 1.23×10^2
   b) 4.5×10^3
   c) 7.5×10^5
   d) 1.25×10^6
   e) 2.5×10^{-1}
   f) 5.6×10^{-3}
   g) 2×10^{-7}

3. Add the following and express the final answer in scientific notation:

   $4.5 \times 10^3 + 6.8 \times 10^3$

4. Add the following and express the final answer in scientific notation:

   $4.5 \times 10^3 + 3.4 \times 10^4$

5. Express the following numbers as power of ten:

   a) 100,000
   b) 10,000,000
   c) 0.00001
   d) 0.01

6. Express the following numbers as power of ten:

   a) 1
   b) 100
   c) 0.1
   d) 1000
   e) 0.0001

f) 1,000,000

7. Perform the following operations and express your answer as a power of ten using scientific notation:

a) $300 + 75{,}000$
b) $5 \times 10^4 + 25 \times 10^3$
c) $0.2 \times 10^{-2} - 4 \times 10^{-3}$
d) $3 \times 10^3 - 250 \times 10^2 + 0.07 \times 10^4$
e) $4000 - 850$

8. Perform the following operations and express your answer as a power of ten using scientific notation:

a) $0.1 \times 10^3 - 0.001 \times 10^5$
b) $100 \times 10^{-1} + 0.12 \times 10^4$
c) $10^3 + 10^4$
d) $18.3 \times 10^6 + 7.7 \times 10^8$
e) $10^1 - 0.003 \times 10^4$

9. Perform the following operations and express your answer as a power of ten using engineering notation:

a) $(10) \times (1000)$
b) $(0.1) \times (100)$
c) $(10^3) \times (10^5)$
d) $(10000) \times (10^{-4})$
e) $(10^{-3}) \times (10^5) \times (10^2)$

10. Perform the following operations and express your answer as a power of ten using engineering notation:

a) $(100000000) \times (0.0000001)$
b) $(0.01) \times (1000)$
c) $(100000) \times (10^{-6})$
d) $(0.0001) \times (0.001)$
e) $(0.1) \times (0.01) \times (0.0001)$

11. Perform the following operations and express your answer in scientific notation:

a) $(20{,}000) \times (0.0002)$
b) $1100 \times (0.001)$
c) $(0.000076) \times (1{,}600{,}000)$
d) $(20 \times 10^{-3}) \times (0.008) \times (3 \times 10^5)$
e) $(0.044) \times (0.006)$

12. Perform the following operations and express your answer in engineering notation:

a) $\dfrac{100}{100,000}$

b) $\dfrac{0.001}{0.00001}$

c) $\dfrac{0.00000001}{10,000}$

d) $\dfrac{1,000,000}{1,000}$

e) $\dfrac{10^{\frac{3}{2}}}{10^{\frac{-1}{2}}}$

13. Perform the following operations and express your answer in engineering notation:

a) $\dfrac{7000}{0.00006}$

b) $\dfrac{0.005}{50,000}$

c) $\dfrac{0.000330}{0.00002}$

d) $\dfrac{72}{648}$

e) $\dfrac{52 \times 10^5}{26 \times 10^3}$

14. Perform the following operations and express your answer in engineering notation:

a) $(1000)^6$

b) $(0.0001)^{1/3}$

c) $(10,000)^9$

d) $(0.00001)^6$

e) $(10)^{1/2}$

15. Perform the following operations and express your answer in scientific notation:

  a) $(100)^3$

  b) $(500,000)^{1/5}$

  c) $(0.001)^2$

  d) $(0.1)^{1/4}$

  e) $(0.0001)^{1/2}$

16. Perform the following operations and express your answer in scientific notation:

  a) $(-0.01)^2$

  b) $\dfrac{(1000) \times (10^{-3})}{100}$

  c) $\dfrac{(0.001)^2 \times (1000)}{10,000}$

  d) $\dfrac{(10^6) \times (10^{-3})}{0.0001}$

  e) $\dfrac{(0.1)^2 \times (100)}{0.01}$

  f) $\dfrac{[(100) \times (0.01)]^{-2}}{(10)^2 \times (0.01)}$

17. Perform the following operations and express your answer in engineering notation:

  a) $(10)^3$

b) $-\dfrac{(10^7) \times (10^{-5})}{0.01}$

c) $\dfrac{(3000)^2 \times (.01)}{100,000}$

d) $\dfrac{(5)^2}{(0.05)^{1/2}}$

e) $[0.000025]^{1/2} \times [100]^3 \times [0.01]$

f) $\dfrac{\{(0.001)^3\} \times \{0.005\}^{-2} \times \{(25)^2\}}{\{(400) \times (0.006)\}^{-1/2}}$

18. Fill in the blanks of the following conversions:

a) $5 \times 10^3 = \underline{\hspace{1cm}} \times 10^6$

b) $2 \times 10^{-6} = \underline{\hspace{1cm}} \times 10^{-3}$

c) $25 \times 10^3 = \underline{\hspace{1cm}} \times 10^{-3} = \underline{\hspace{1cm}} \times 10^{-6}$

d) $100 \times 10^0 = \underline{\hspace{1cm}} \times 10^{-3} = \underline{\hspace{1cm}} \times 10^3 = \underline{\hspace{1cm}} \times 10^6$

e) $0.001 = \underline{\hspace{1cm}} \times 10^{-3} = \underline{\hspace{1cm}} \times 10^{-6} = \underline{\hspace{1cm}} \times 10^3 = \underline{\hspace{1cm}} \times 10^{-9} = \underline{\hspace{1cm}} \times 10^6$

19. Express the data in Scientific Notation with one nonzero digit to the left of the decimal.

a. 154.65	**b.** 300.85	**c.** 940.01	**d.** 80 000.2
e. 80000	**f.** 0.0017	**g.** 8.00065	**h.** 4000.
i. 5500	**j.** 5500.	**k.** 1800.0	**l.** 4000.0
m. 0.0204	**n.** 0.2100	**o.** 0.0091400	

20. Express the data in Scientific Notation with one nonzero digit to the left of the decimal.

a. 2700	**b.** 4400	**c.** 490.06	**d.** 8700.0
e. 60000	**f.** 0.0071	**g.** 0.7800	**h.** 7000.
i. 200.58	**j.** 658.93	**k.** 60000.7	**l.** 0.0905
m. 3000.0	**n.** 3.00056	**o.** 0.0027900	

21. Find the equivalent fractions using the indicated denominators.

    a) $\dfrac{3}{4} = \dfrac{?}{32}$

    b) $\dfrac{2}{3} = \dfrac{?}{15}$

    c) $\dfrac{7}{8} = \dfrac{?}{64}$

22. Reduce each fraction to the lowest terms.

    a) $\dfrac{8}{12}$

    b) $\dfrac{34}{64}$

    c) $\dfrac{2}{8}$

23. Change the decimals to fractions in the lowest terms.

    a) 0.0125

    b) 0.83

    c) 0.001

    d) 0.872

24. Change the fractions to decimals. If necessary, round to the nearest hundredth.

    a) $\dfrac{1}{5}$

    b) $\dfrac{1}{10}$

    c) $\dfrac{2}{7}$

d) $\dfrac{15}{16}$

25. Write the improper fractions as whole or mixed numbers.

   a) $\dfrac{9}{3}$

   b) $\dfrac{39}{8}$ -

   c) $\dfrac{27}{6}$

   d) $\dfrac{22}{7}$

   e) $\dfrac{43}{8}$

26. Add the following fractions and reduce to the lowest terms. Convert improper fractions to whole or mixed numbers.

   a) $\dfrac{5}{16} + \dfrac{1}{16}$

   b) $\dfrac{3}{8} + \dfrac{1}{8}$

   c) $3\dfrac{1}{3} + 1\dfrac{7}{16}$

   d) $\dfrac{1}{6} + \dfrac{7}{9} + \dfrac{2}{3}$

   e) $4\dfrac{1}{2} + 9$

   f) $1\dfrac{5}{8} + 2\dfrac{1}{2}$

27. Subtract the following fractions and reduce to the lowest terms. Convert improper fractions to whole or mixed numbers.

a) $\dfrac{7}{8} - \dfrac{5}{8}$

b) $\dfrac{7}{16} - \dfrac{3}{8}$

c) $\dfrac{3}{8} - \dfrac{7}{32}$

d) $9\dfrac{1}{32} - 3\dfrac{3}{8}$

28. Multiply and reduce answers to lowest terms. Convert improper fractions to whole or mixed numbers.

a) $\dfrac{3}{10} \times \dfrac{4}{15}$

b) $\dfrac{7}{12} \times \dfrac{4}{5}$

c) $\dfrac{1}{2} \times \dfrac{3}{4} \times \dfrac{8}{9}$

d) $\dfrac{3}{8} \times \dfrac{5}{6} \times \dfrac{1}{2}$

e) $\dfrac{1}{5} \times 7\dfrac{5}{8}$

f) $\dfrac{2}{3} \times 3\dfrac{1}{4}$

29. Divide and reduce answers to lowest terms. Convert improper fractions to whole or mixed numbers.

a) $\dfrac{1}{2} \div \dfrac{7}{12}$

b) $\dfrac{1}{5} \div \dfrac{1}{2}$

c) $8 \div \dfrac{1}{4}$

d) $2\dfrac{1}{2} \div 4$

e) $2\dfrac{2}{9} \div 1\dfrac{2}{3}$

30. A fruit-stand owner mixes $10\dfrac{3}{4}$ lb of apples, 20 lb of oranges, and $8\dfrac{1}{2}$ lb of bananas. What is the total weight of the mixed fruit?

31. If $6\dfrac{1}{4}$ ft of wire is needed to make one extension cord, how many extension cords can be made from $68\dfrac{3}{4}$ ft of wire?

32. Marlene needs $3\dfrac{1}{3}$ yd of red velvet to make a dress. How many yards she needs to make two dresses?

33. A baker has $5\dfrac{1}{2}$ cups of sugar on hand to make a batch of cookies requiring $1\dfrac{2}{3}$ cups of sugar. How much sugar is left over?

34. Change the fractions to percent equivalents:

a) $1\dfrac{1}{4}$

b) $3\dfrac{2}{3}$

c) 5.3

d) 5.12

35. Change the percent to their fraction and decimal equivalents: 75%, 38%, and 5%.

36. Change the numbers to their percent equivalents.

   a) $\dfrac{7}{1000}$

   b) $3\dfrac{1}{2}$

   c) 15.1

   d) $1\dfrac{1}{3}$

   e) 36.25

   f) $3\dfrac{1}{2}$

37. Change the percent to both fractional and decimal equivalents.

   a) 18.75%

   b) $\dfrac{1}{5}\%$

   c) 45%

   d) 0.05%

   e) $66\dfrac{2}{3}\%$

38. $\dfrac{1}{4}\%$ of 875 is what number?

39. 325% of 86 is what number?

40. Estimate a 15% tip on a restaurant bill of $48.00.

41. A taxi fare is $24.00. Find the amount of a 20% tip.

42. 20% of what number is 45?

43. If a type of solder contains 55% tin, how many pounds of tin are needed to make 10 lb. of solder?

44. If a 150-horsepower (hp) engine delivers only 110 hp to the driving wheels of a car, what is the efficiency of the engine?

45. The effective value of current or voltage in an ac circuit is 71.3% of the maximum voltage. If a voltmeter shows a voltage of 110 volts (V) as the effective value in a circuit, what is the maximum voltage?

46. A motorist with an annual income of $18,250 spends each year $3,420 on automobile financing, $652 on gasoline, $625 on insurance, and $150 on maintenance and repair. What percent of the motor's annual income is used for automotive transportation?

47. There are 25 women in a class of 60 students. Find the percent of men in the class.

48. A 78-lb alloy of tin, copper and silver have 50 lb of tin and 12 lb of copper. Find the percent of silver in the alloy.

49. If a dress is marked 25% off the original price, what percent of the original price does the buyer pay?

50. An engine that has a 4% loss of power has an output of 336 hp. What is the input (base) horsepower of the engine?

51. Melissa Silvers was earning $90,000 and received a 10% raise. Find her new annual earning.

52. $\frac{1}{8}$% of 320 is what number?

53. Find the sales tax and the total bill on an order of DVDs costing $121.72 if the tax rate is 8%.

54. Tammy has net salary of $1,000.00 and a gross salary of $1500.00. What percent of the gross salary is the total of the deductions?

55. Cast iron contains 4.25% carbon. How much carbon is contained in a 25-lb bar of cast iron?

56. An engine operating at 91% efficiency transmits 170 hp. What is the engine's maximum capacity (base) in horsepower?

57. The voltage of a motor is 110 Volts. If 9 Volts are lost, what is the rate of voltage lost?

58. Gertrude earns $6,150 in one pay period. Medicare tax is 1.52% of the earnings. How much is deducted for Medicare tax?

59. Dora receives 6% commission on all sales made as an Avon lady. If she sells $100,000 in merchandise during a given period, what is the commission?

60. Beulah is paid a salary of $12,000 monthly as a corporate consultant of a small investment firm plus a 1% of the net earnings of the business. Find the total salary of a month when the net earnings of the business is $10,000,000.

61. The city of Metropolis has 1,285, 792 people living within its city limits. If the population is expected to grow by 25% over the next year, how many new people will be living there? What is the total number of people living in that year?

62. Compute the % error if the calculated voltage in a circuit is 30 and the measured value is 29.5.

63. Solve for x in the following equation: $3x + 6 = 12$.

64. Find the unknown variable z in the following equation: $-6z - 24 = -2z -36$.

65. What is the value of t in the following equation: $2t = 10$?

66. Solve for the variable u.

$u - 3 = 2u + 3$

67. Find the unknown variable a in the following equation: $\dfrac{-a}{2} - 3 = 7$

68. Find the unknown variable j in the following equation: $\dfrac{-3j}{4} + 2 = -1$

69. What is the value of p in the following equation?

$3p - \dfrac{1}{4} = 2$

70. Solve for the variable s.

$\dfrac{1}{s} = 3$

71. Find the unknown variable c in the following equation.

$$\frac{2-c}{3} + 3 = 6$$

72. Find R in the following equation.

$$\frac{1}{R} = \frac{1}{3} + \frac{1}{4}$$

73. Solve for the variable v.

$$\frac{1}{v} - 1 = 9$$

74. Solve for the variable d in the equation below.

$$-\frac{1}{2d+1} + 2 = -3$$

75. Solve for the variable x in the following equation.

$$4 + \frac{16}{3-x} = 12$$

76. What is the value of g in the equation below?

$$\frac{g-2}{5} = 4$$

77. Solve for w in the following equation: $2w - 6 = \frac{-3w+6}{4} - 2$

78. Solve for the variable y in the equation below.

$$\frac{1}{2} = \frac{1}{2y} + \frac{4}{4y}$$

79. Solve for angle θ in degrees. Round off your answer to the nearest hundredth.

$$7 \sin(\theta) = 6$$

80. Solve for angle β in degrees. Round off your answer to the nearest hundredth.

$$10 \cos (\beta) = 5$$

81. Solve for angle α in degrees. Round off your answer to the nearest hundredth.

$$\frac{3}{\tan(\alpha)} = 15$$

82. Solve for angle δ in degrees. Round off your answer to the nearest hundredth.

$$\frac{2}{\cos(\delta)} + 5 = 2$$

83. Solve for angle γ in degrees. Round off your answer to the nearest hundredth.

$$\frac{\sin(\gamma)}{4} - 0.04 = 0.05$$

84. In a right triangle, all three angles add up to $180°$. Suppose that a right triangle has angles, χ (Chi), ψ (Psi) and τ (Tau). What is the angle of τ, if χ is $90°$ and ψ is $30°$?

85. In physics, the speed of light (c) is directly proportional to the wavelength (λ) and frequency (f) in an equation $c = f \times \lambda$. Compute the value of λ if c is 3×10^8 and f is 100,000.

86. In an electrical circuit, the current is inversely proportional to the resistance (R) and directly proportional to the voltage (V) in an equation called Ohm's Law $\left[I = \frac{V}{R} \right]$. Solve for R, if I = 0.001 and V = 20.

87. In a DC electrical circuit, the power (P), voltage (V) and resistance (R) are governed by the following equation: $\left[P = \frac{V^2}{R} \right]$. Compute the value of R if V = 25 and P = 0.15.

88. Using the same equation from Problem 25, solve for V when R = 500 and P = 2.5.

89. In a DC electrical circuit, the power (P), current (I) and resistance (R) are governed by the following equation: $P = I^2 R$. Compute the value of R if I = 0.025 and P = 0.75.

90. Using the same equation from Problem 27, solve for I when R = 10 and P = 30.

91. Power (P), energy (E_n) and time (t) are related by the following equation: $P = \dfrac{E_n}{t}$.

   If P = 15 and E_n = 45, what is the value of t?

92. In electric circuits, charge (C), is directly proportional to current (I) and inversely proportional to time (t). This relationship is shown in the following equation: $I = \dfrac{Q}{t}$.
   Compute the value of t, when I = 0.0090 and Q = 0.0002.

93. Using the same equation from Problem 30, compute Q, when I = .008 and $t = 3 \times 10^{-3}$.

94. In Electronic Communications, the modulation of index (m) is related to the Modulating Voltage (E_m) and the Carrier Voltage (E_c) by the following equation: $m = \dfrac{E_m}{E_c}$. What is the value of m if E_c = 25 and E_m = 20.

95. Convert the modulation index (m) computed in Problem 32 to a percent.

96. The current gain (β) of a BJT transistor is related to the collector current (I_C) and the base current (I_B) by the following equation $\beta = \dfrac{I_C}{I_B}$. Compute I_B if β = 1000 and I_C = .00845. Write your answer in Scientific Notation.

97. Compute the value of I_C from Problem 34, if β = 100,000 and $I_B = 3 \times 10^{-3}$.

98. The efficiency (η) of a motor is related to the Input Power (P_{in}) going into the motor and the Output Power (P_{out}) coming out of the motor. The following equation shows the relationship: $\eta = \dfrac{P_{out}}{P_{in}}$.

   a) Compute the value of η, if P_{in} = 100,000 and P_{out} = 90,000.

   b) Compute the value of P_{in}, when P_{out} = 800 and η = 0.95.

   c) Calculate the value of P_{out}, for P_{in} = 16 and η = 65%

   d) Express the value of η as a percent (%) in part a) of this question.

99. In Electric Power and Machinery, the synchronous speed of a motor (η_s) is directly proportional to the frequency (f) and inversely proportional to the number of poles of the motor (p). This equation for this relationship is shown below.

$$\eta_s = \frac{120 \times f}{p}$$

a) Compute the value of η_s, when $f = 60$ and $p = 6$.

b) Compute the value of f, when $p = 4$ and $\eta_s = 1500$.

c) Compute the number of poles (p), when $f = 60$ and $\eta_s = 3600$.

100. In an induction motor, the slip (s) is defined as the percentage difference between synchronous speed (η_s) and the actual speed (n) that the motor is turning. The relationship of the variables is shown below.

$$s = \frac{\eta_s - n}{\eta_s}$$

a) Compute the value of the slip (s) when $\eta_s = 1800$ and n = 1760.

b) Express the value of s computed in part a) as a percent.

c) If the slip is given as 4% and η_s is 1500, compute the value of n.

d) If the slip is 0.0125 and n is 1185, what is the value of (η_s)?

101. In Electronics, the two possible states for a single diode is on and off. For multiple diodes in an electronic circuit, the equation is governed by $X = 2^n$. The variable n represents the number of diodes and X represents the total number of possible states.

a) What are the possible number of states when three diodes are present in the electronic circuit?

b) How many diodes are present in the circuit, if 16 total states are possible?

102. Solve for R_T in terms of R.

$$\frac{1}{R_T} = \frac{1}{3R} + \frac{1}{7R}$$

103. The equations below are used to calculate the temperatures in Celsius (°C) and Fahrenheit (°F). T_C represents the temperature in Celsius. T_F represents the temperature in Fahrenheit.

$$T_C = \frac{5}{9}\left(T_F - 32°\right)$$

$$T_F = \frac{9}{5}\left(T_C + 32°\right)$$

a) What is 75°F on the Celsius temperature scale?

b) What is 20°C on the Fahrenheit temperature scale?

104. The distance traveled by an object is directly proportional to both the rate and time associated with that object. The variable for the distance is d. The variable for the rate is v. The variable for time is t. Find the rate of a car that moved a distance of 385 miles in 7 hours using the equation below.

$$d = v \times t$$

105. Gasoline moves through a pipeline at 40 gal per minute. How many gallons per hour can move through the pipeline?

106. A toll station can accommodate on average 30 vehicles per minute. How many vehicles can be accommodated in an hour?

107. For the following matrix, find the cofactors of a_{21}, a_{33}, and a_{13}.

$$\begin{bmatrix} 4 & 1 & 2 \\ 3 & -1 & 2 \\ 6 & -1 & 0 \end{bmatrix}$$

108. Find the cofactors of a_{31}, a_{11}, and a_{23} of the matrix given in Problem 1.

109. Find the cofactors of a_{22}, a_{13}, and a_{21} of the matrix given in Problem 1.

110. Find the cofactors of a_{12}, a_{32}, and a_{33} of the matrix given in Problem 1.

111. Find all cofactors of the following matrix.

$$\begin{bmatrix} 1 & -1 \\ 3 & 2 \end{bmatrix}$$

112. Find the determinant of the matrix below.

$$\mathbf{A} = \begin{bmatrix} 3 & 1 \\ 2 & -4 \end{bmatrix}$$

113. Find the determinant of the matrix below.

$$\mathbf{A} = \begin{bmatrix} 4 & -6 \\ 1 & 1 \end{bmatrix}$$

114. Find the determinant of the matrix below.

$$\mathbf{A} = \begin{bmatrix} 1 & 2 & 3 \\ 0 & 0 & -1 \\ 4 & -2 & 0 \end{bmatrix}$$

115. Find the determinant of the matrix below.

$$\mathbf{A} = \begin{bmatrix} 2 & -1 & 3 \\ 0 & 1 & 2 \\ 3 & -2 & 1 \end{bmatrix}$$

116. Find the determinant of the matrix below.

$$\mathbf{A} = \begin{bmatrix} s-2 & 4 & 3 \\ 1 & s+1 & -2 \\ 0 & 0 & s-4 \end{bmatrix}$$

117. Find the determinant of the matrix below.

$$\mathbf{A} = \begin{bmatrix} 1 & 2 & 2 & 3 \\ 1 & 0 & -2 & 0 \\ 3 & -1 & 1 & -2 \\ 4 & -3 & 0 & 2 \end{bmatrix}$$

118. Perform the following expression.

$$\begin{bmatrix} 1 & 7 \\ 2 & 6 \end{bmatrix} + \begin{bmatrix} 3 & 5 \\ 1 & 1 \end{bmatrix}$$

119. Perform the following expression.

$$\begin{bmatrix} 7 & 6 & 6 \\ 5 & 4 & 1 \\ 9 & 8 & 2 \end{bmatrix} - \begin{bmatrix} 1 & 0 & 0 \\ 0 & 1 & 0 \\ 0 & 0 & 1 \end{bmatrix}$$

120. Perform the following expressions.

$$\begin{bmatrix} 2 & 1 \\ 0 & 0 \end{bmatrix} \times \begin{bmatrix} 3 & 2 \\ 1 & 1 \end{bmatrix}$$

121. Perform the following expression.

$$\begin{bmatrix} 1 & 9 \\ 7 & 2 \end{bmatrix} \times \begin{bmatrix} 2 & 1 & 3 \\ 4 & -1 & -7 \end{bmatrix}$$

122. Perform the following expression.

$$\begin{bmatrix} 1 & 2 & -3 & 4 \\ 0 & -5 & -1 & -2 \end{bmatrix} \times \begin{bmatrix} 2 & -5 \\ 3 & 0 \\ 6 & 1 \\ -2 & 3 \end{bmatrix}$$

123. Perform the following expression.

$$\begin{bmatrix} 2 & 3 \\ -5 & 0 \\ 1 & -4 \end{bmatrix} - \begin{bmatrix} 1 & 0 \\ -2 & -1 \\ -3 & 5 \end{bmatrix} + \begin{bmatrix} 0 & 1 \\ 1 & -1 \\ -2 & -1 \end{bmatrix}$$

124. Perform the following expression.

$$\begin{bmatrix} 1 & 6 \\ -3 & 4 \end{bmatrix} \times \begin{bmatrix} -1 & 0 \\ 3 & 2 \end{bmatrix}$$

125. Perform the following expression.

$$\begin{bmatrix} 2 & -1 \end{bmatrix} \times \begin{bmatrix} -4 \\ -5 \end{bmatrix}$$

126. Perform the following expression.

$$\begin{bmatrix} 3 \\ -1 \end{bmatrix} \times \begin{bmatrix} 2 & 5 \end{bmatrix}$$

QUESTIONS 127- 137 refer to the following matrices

$$A = \begin{bmatrix} 2 & 0 & 4 \\ 1 & 4 & -1 \\ 3 & 1 & 2 \end{bmatrix} \quad B = \begin{bmatrix} 3 & 5 & 2 \\ 0 & 8 & 4 \\ 1 & 0 & 9 \end{bmatrix}$$

$$C = \begin{bmatrix} 1 \\ 2 \\ 3 \end{bmatrix} \quad D = \begin{bmatrix} 1 & 4 \\ -2 & 3 \end{bmatrix}$$

127. What is the transpose of **A**?

128. Solve for the determinant of **A**.

129. Calculate the inverse of **D**.

130. What is the product of **A** × **C**?

131. What is the rank of **B**?

132. Compute the sum of **A** + **B**.

133. What is the product of **3** × **D**?

134. Calculate the product of **C** × **D**.

135. Write a set of equations that describe the matrix equation **A**×**X** = **C**.

136. Show that **A** + **B** = **B** + **A**.

137. Show that **A** × **B** ≠ **B** × **A**

138. What is the rank of the following matrix?

$$\begin{bmatrix} 2 & 1 & 1 \\ 1 & 1 & 1 \\ 3 & 2 & 1 \end{bmatrix}$$

139. Given the following matrix:

$$A = \begin{bmatrix} 1 & 2 & 0 \\ 3 & -1 & 1 \\ 0 & 2 & 0 \end{bmatrix}$$

a) compute the determinant.

b) find the rank.

140. Solve the simultaneous linear equations by using the following methods:

a) Substitution Method
b) Algebraic Elimination Method
c) Cramer's Rule Method

$$2x - 3y = 5$$
$$3x + 7y = -2$$

141. Solve the set of simultaneous linear equations by using the Cramer's Rule Method.

$$3z + 2y = x + 1$$
$$3y + 2x = 8 - 5z$$
$$3x - 1 = y - 2z$$

142. Given the following system of simultaneous equations:

$$4i_1 + 2i_2 = -2$$
$$5i_1 + 3i_2 = 2$$

a) Substitution Method
b) Algebraic Elimination Method
c) Cramer's Rule Method

143.   Given the following system of simultaneous equations:

$$2x + 3y = -5$$
$$\frac{1}{2}x + 2y = 3$$

    a) Substitution Method
    b) Algebraic Elimination Method
    c) Cramer's Rule Method

144. Given the following system of simultaneous equations:

$$V_1 + \frac{1}{2}V_2 = -5$$

$$-\frac{1}{2}V_1 - 2V_2 = -15$$

    a) Substitution Method
    b) Algebraic Elimination Method
    c) Cramer's Rule Method

145. Given the following system of simultaneous equations:

$$5R + 3V = 4$$
$$2R + 5V = \frac{1}{2}$$

    a) Substitution Method
    b) Algebraic Elimination Method
    c) Cramer's Rule Method

146. Given the following system of simultaneous equations:

$$\frac{1}{2}a + 2b = 4$$
$$2a + \frac{1}{2}b = 5$$

    a) Substitution Method

b) Algebraic Elimination Method

c) Cramer's Rule Method

147. Given the following system of simultaneous equations:

$$3a + b = 7$$
$$-\frac{1}{2}a - 2b = 9$$

a) Substitution Method

b) Algebraic Elimination Method

c) Cramer's Rule Method

148. Given the following system of simultaneous equations:

$$-2R + 3V = -1$$

$$2R - 3V = -\frac{1}{2}$$

a) Substitution Method

b) Algebraic Elimination Method

c) Cramer's Rule Method

149. Solve the set of linear algebraic equations by using the Gauss Jordan Elimination Method.

$$x - y = 1$$

$$x + y - 2z = -3$$

$$y + z = 5$$

150. Solve for the eigenvalues and eigenvectors of the matrix **A** without using MATLAB?

$$A = \begin{bmatrix} 1 & 4 \\ 2 & 3 \end{bmatrix}$$

151. Solve for the eigenvalues and eigenvectors of the matrix **C** without using MATLAB?

$$C = \begin{bmatrix} 3 & 5 \\ 2 & 4 \end{bmatrix}$$

152. Use MATLAB to find the eigenvalues and eigenvectors of the matrix **A**?

$$A = \begin{bmatrix} 2 & 3 & 5 \\ 1 & 1 & 1 \\ 5 & 9 & 4 \end{bmatrix}$$

153. Use MATLAB to find the eigenvalues and eigenvectors of the matrix **A**?

$$A = \begin{bmatrix} 6 & 10 \\ 5 & 12 \end{bmatrix}$$

HOMEWORK FOR CHAPTER 8

1. Convert 5.5×10^{-4} *seconds* to *μs*.

2. Change 0.034 m^2 to cm^2.

3. Change 1.20 *μs* to *ms*.

4. Convert 220 *μs* to *ms*.

5. Convert 400 *g* to *kg*.

6. Change 1500 *m* to *km*.

7. Change 0.023 *cm* to *mm*.

8. Convert 87 *mg* to *g*.

9. Convert 0.00068 *s* to *μs*.

10. Change 4100 *mm* to *m*.

11. Convert 0.0067 *km* to *cm*.

12. Change 0.06 m^2 to cm^2.

13. Change 55.0 mm^2 to cm^2.

14. Convert 10 cm^2 to mm^2.

15. Convert 8600 cm^2 to m^2.

16. Perform the following conversion: 0.05 *s* to *milli-seconds* (*ms*).

17. Perform the following conversion: 2000 *μs* to *milli-seconds* (*ms*).

18. Perform the following conversion: 0.04 *ms* to *micro-seconds* (*μs*).

19. Perform the following conversion: 8400 *ps* to micro-seconds (*μs*)

20. Perform the following conversion: 4×10^{-3} *km* to *milli-meters* (*mm*).

21. Perform the following conversion: 260×10^3 *mm* to *kilo-meters* (*km*).

22. What is a mile in feet (ft), yards (yd), meters (m), and kilo-meters (km)?

23. The speed of light is defined as 299,792,458 m/s. Convert the speed of light to miles per hours (mph).

24. How long in seconds will it take a car traveling at 60 mph to travel the length of a football field (100 yd)?

25. Convert 30 mph to meters per second (m/s).

26. If an athlete can row at a rate of 50 yd/min, how many days would it take to cross the width of the Atlantic Ocean, which expands 1,770 miles (mi)?

27. The Pacific Ocean expands 9,600 miles (mi). Convert this distance to kilo-meters (km).

28. How many hours would it take a speedboat moving at 120 mph to cross the Indian Ocean which is 6,200 miles wide?

29. How long will it take a runner to complete a 10 km race if a pace of 6.5 mi/min was maintained?

30. Quarters are about 1 inch in diameter. How many would be required to stretch from one end of a football field to the other (100 yd)?

31. Compare the total time required to drive 100 miles at an average speed of 60 mph versus an average speed of 75 mph.

32. Find the distance in meters that an object traveling at 500 cm/s will cover in 0.035 h.

33. How many cubic centi-meters (cm^3) are in a 40 oz bottle of Budweiser?

34. How many pints are in 1 m^3 of water?

35. How many seconds and minutes are in 2 days?

36. How many *British thermal units* (*BTU*) are in 10 *Joules* (*J*) of energy?

37. Convert 34 *kg* to pounds (*lb*).

38. Change 28 *feet* (*ft*) to *meters* (*m*).

39. Convert 25 *joules* (*J*) *to ft-pounds* (*ft-lb*).

40. Change 8.6 *inches* (*in.*) to *mm*.

41. How much *horsepower* (*hp*) are in 37 *kW*.

42. Change 55 *m* to *ft*.

43. Change 3.6 *kg* to *lb*.

44. Change 120 *lb* to *kg*.

45. Convert 150 *ft* to *m*.

46. Convert 1000 *W* to *hp*.

47. Convert 12,000 *J* to *BTU*.

48. Change 0.25 *hp* to *Watts* (*W*).

49. Convert 12 *ft-lb* to *Joules* (*J*).

50. Change 23 m^2 to ft^2.

51. Convert 35 $\dfrac{m}{s}$ to $\dfrac{ft}{s}$

52. Change 0.55 *lb* to *g*.

53. Perform the following conversion: 0.1 *μF* to *pico-farads* (*pF*).

54. Perform the following conversion: 80 *mm* to *centi-meters* (*cm*).

55. Perform the following conversion: 60 *cm* to *kilo-meters* (*km*).

56. Perform the following conversion: 3.2 *h* to *milli-seconds* (*ms*).

57. Perform the following conversion: 0.016 *mm* to *micro-meters* (*μm*).

58. Perform the following conversion: 60 sq *cm* (cm^2) to square meters (m^2).

59. How many ounces of Coca-Cola soft drink can be filled in a 3 liter bottles?

60. How many cubic meters (m^3) are needed to fill 1000 Liter (L) tank?

61. Change the following unit from: 8,908.96 $\dfrac{in}{year}$ to $\dfrac{mm}{min}$.

62. Change the following unit from: 6,598 $\dfrac{kW}{h}$ to $\dfrac{hp}{s}$.

63. Change the following unit from: $7,545 \dfrac{m}{year}$ to $\dfrac{ft}{decade}$.

64. Change the following unit from: $7,777.7 \dfrac{kg}{yd}$ to $\dfrac{lb}{in}$.

65. Change the following unit from: $12,555 \dfrac{lb}{mi}$ to $\dfrac{kg}{ft}$.

66. Change the following unit from: $5,654 \dfrac{ft}{s}$ to $\dfrac{m}{yr}$.

67. Change the following unit from: $12,536 \dfrac{W}{min}$ to $\dfrac{hp}{s}$.

68. Change the following unit from: 18,569 Joules (J) to *British thermal units (Btu)*.

69. Convert 12,560.15 *horsepower (hp)* to *Watts (W)*.

70. Convert 7,128 *foot-pound (ft-lb)* to *Joules (J)*.

71. Convert 88 *seconds (sec)* to *minutes (min)*.

72. Suppose that Sarah walks along a hiking trail at $2\dfrac{mi}{hr}$.

   a) What is her rate in $\dfrac{mi}{day}$?

   b) How many days will it take for her to reach a destination that is $14\dfrac{1}{2}$ miles away?

   c) If she started hiking at 6:00 am, what time will she reach her destination?

73. Suppose that Sarah decides to ride her bicycle next time instead of walking as she did in Problem 72. Suppose that she rides her bicycle at a speed of $15\ \dfrac{mi}{hr}$.

    a) What is her rate in $\dfrac{mi}{day}$?

    b) How many days will it take for her to reach a destination that is $14\dfrac{1}{2}$ miles away?

    c) If she started bicycling at 6:00 am, what time will she reach her destination?

74. Suppose that Sarah decides to ride her thoroughbred horse this time instead of hiking or bicycling as she did in Problem 72 and Problem 73. Suppose that the horse gallops at a rate of $30\ \dfrac{mi}{hr}$.

    a) What is her rate in $\dfrac{mi}{day}$?

    b) How many days will it take for her to reach a destination that is $14\dfrac{1}{2}$ miles away?

    c) If she started horse riding at 6:00 am, what time will she reach her destination?

75. Suppose that Sarah of Problem 72 decides to drive a car instead of walking, bicycling or horse riding to reach her destination. Instead she drives her Jaguar at 55 mph.

    a) How many days will it take for her to reach the same destination that of $14\dfrac{1}{2}$ miles away?

    b) If she started driving at 6:00 am, what time will she reach her destination?

76. Refer to Problems 72 – 75 in answering these questions.

    a) How much time did Sarah save by riding her bicycle instead of hiking?

    b) How much time did Sarah save by riding her horse instead of bicycling?

    c) How much time did Sarah save by driving her Jaguar instead of riding her horse?

d) How much time did Sarah save by driving her Jaguar instead of hiking?

77. The Super Bowl football game is being played at 6:00 pm [EST] in Miami, Florida. Marcus intends to watch the Super Bowl live from his hotel room in Tokyo, Japan. What time will it be on TV on Tokyo's local time?

78. Darlene's plane leaves Denver, Colorado at 5:00 pm and arrives in New York City at 6:15 pm. How many hours was her flight?

79. Latoya is on vacation in Honolulu, Hawaii. She plans to call her girlfriend, Keisha who lives back home in Atlanta, Georgia. Keisha wants to talk with Latoya at 9:00 pm. What time should Latoya call Keisha?

80. Jack who is stationed in Baghdad, Iraq called his wife, Irene at 7:00 am who lives in Dallas, Texas. At what time will Irene be expecting Jack's phone call?

81. Time in Jerusalem, Israel, is defined as (+2 GMT) and time in Buenos Aires, Argentina, is defined as (-3 GMT). If it is 10:00 am in Jerusalem, what time is it in Buenos Aires?

82. Agnes's travel itinerary indicates that she will leave Los, Angeles, California, at 3:05 pm and arrive in Chicago, Illinois at 4:35 pm on a nonstop flight, what is the flight time?

83. Maxine, who lives in Atlanta, Georgia, has an interview with Waste Management, Inc. which is located in Houston Texas. Delta Airlines told her that the flight time would be one hour and twenty-four minutes. What is her arrival time in Houston, if she leaves at 12:20 pm?

84. Ms. Victoria Kimura attends the United States International University in Nairobi, Kenya. She accepted an interview with Wachovia Corporation in Charlotte, North Carolina.

a) What is the difference in time between the two cities?

b) Suppose that Victoria got a direct flight from Nairobi to Charlotte, and she left at 6:00 am, what time will she arrive in Charlotte?

85. If it is 1:00 am in London, England, what time is it in Phoenix, Arizona?

86. If it is 4:00 pm in Edinburgh, Scotland, what time is it in Istanbul, Turkey?

87. Mary's travel itinerary indicates that she is to leave Memphis, Tennessee, at 4:00 pm and arrive in Amsterdam, The Netherlands, at 7:00 am on a nonstop flight, how many hours will she have to fly?

88. Business executives in New York City, Saint Louis, and London England want to schedule a conference call between 8 am and 4 pm local time. What range of hours can be used to schedule the meeting according to the local time in each city?

HOMEWORK FOR CHAPTER 9

1. Plot the function $f(t) = -3t + 2$ over the interval $[-5,-4,-3,-2,-1,0,1,2,3,4,5]$.

2. Plot the $f(t) = t^3$ over the interval $[-3,-2,-1,0,1,2,3]$.

3. Plot the function $f(t) = t^2$ over the interval $[-5,-4,-3,-2,-1,0,1,2,3,4,5]$.

4. Plot the function $f(t) = 2t + 5$ over the interval $[-5,-4,-3,-2,-1,0,1,2,3,4,5]$.

5. Plot the function $f(x) = -x - 1$ over the interval $[-10,10]$.

6. Plot the function $f(t) = -\dfrac{t^2}{2}$ over the interval $[-2,-1,0,1,2]$.

7. Plot the function $f(t) = -\dfrac{t^3}{3}$ over the interval $[-3,-2,-1,0,1,2,3]$.

8. Plot the function $f(x) = x + 2$ over the interval $[-4,4]$.

9. Plot the function $f(x) = \dfrac{x-2}{2}$ over the interval $[2,4,6,8,10,12,14,16,18,20]$

10. Plot the function $f(t) = \dfrac{(t-1)^2}{2}$ over the interval $[1,3,5,7,9]$

11. The amount of work, W done in moving an object is the product of the force F and the distance d. Plot the relationship between work and force using the table below.

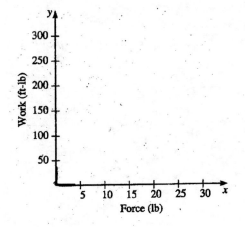

F	W
0	0
5	50
10	100
15	150
20	200
25	250

12. Using the following data, construct a graph using the axis below.

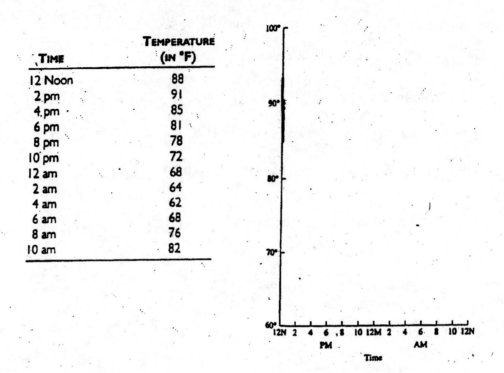

Time	Temperature (in °F)
12 Noon	88
2 pm	91
4 pm	85
6 pm	81
8 pm	78
10 pm	72
12 am	68
2 am	64
4 am	62
6 am	68
8 am	76
10 am	82

13. The following empirical data were gathered concerning the pressure on the bottom of a cylindrical tank exerted by a certain force. Force is the independent variable and pressure is the dependent variable. Plot a graph using the tabulated data.

Force (lb)	0	5	12	25	42	65
Pressure ($1b/in^2$)	0	0.4	1.5	2.7	4	6.5

14. Graph the following empirical data relating the voltage and current of a small light bulb. Voltage is the independent variable and current is the dependent variable.

Voltage (V)	0.1	0.4	0.7	1	2	3
Current (mA)	30	50	60	70	100	135

15. Graph the relationship between the time of day and the corresponding temperature (in degrees Fahrenheit). Time is the independent variable and temperature is the dependent variable.

Time	6:00 am	9:00 am	10:00 am	11:00 am	1:00 pm	3:00 pm	4:00 pm	7:00 pm	10:00 pm
Temp (°F)	35	40	43	50	54	67	65	58	50

16. Graph the following empirical data relating the voltage and current of a light-emitting diode (LED). Voltage is the independent variable and current is the dependent variable.

Voltage (V)	1.4	1.43	1.48	1.5	1.52	1.55	1.6	1.64
Current (mA)	0.01	0.08	0.4	0.6	1.2	1.2	10	30

17. The results of a load test on a DC Series motor are as follows:

E_a (volts)	I_a (amps)	Speed (rpm)	Torque (lb-in)
120	0.40	1800	0.00
120	1.00	1750	3.00
120	1.75	1675	6.00
120	2.40	1625	9.00
120	3.00	1575	12.00

a) Graph the Torque versus Current (I_a).

NOTE: Torque is on the y-axis. Current is on the x-axis.

b) Graph the Speed versus Torque.

NOTE: Torque is on the x-axis. Speed is on the y-axis.

c) Is the torque and current relationship inversely proportional or directly proportional? Explain.

d) Is the torque and speed relationship inversely proportional or directly proportional? Explain.

18. The table below gives the saturation characteristic of a shunt generator. Graph the field current versus the open circuit voltage. Field current is on the x-axis and open circuit voltage is on the y-axis.

Field Current	0	2	4	6	8	10
Open Circuit Voltage	0	80	160	240	280	300

19. For the following points, determine:

(-2,6) and (8,1)

a) the distance between them.

b) the slope of the line passing through them.

c) the midpoint of the line segment joining them.

20. For the following points, determine:

(-3,5) and (-1,-7)

a) the distance between them.

b) the slope of the line passing through them.

c) the midpoint of the line segment joining them.

21. For the following points, determine:

(-6,-5) and (1,-10)

a) the distance between them.

b) the slope of the line passing through them.

c) the midpoint of the line segment joining them.

22. Graph the following equation.

$$y = 3(x - 1) + 4$$

23. Graph the following equation.

$$3x - 2y = 10$$

24. Graph the following equation.

$$y = 16 - 3(x + 4) + 7x$$

25. Solve the following equation graphically.

$$4(x - 1) + 3 = 2x - (5x + 6)$$

26. Solve the following equation graphically.

$$2x + 3(x - 1) = -(x - 5) + 8$$

27. Solve the following equation graphically.

$$8x - 2(3x + 5) = 3x - 9$$

28. Solve the following equation graphically.

$$5x - 3 + 7x = 4(2x + 1)$$

29. Graph the following function.

$$y = 2(3x - 1) + 7 - 3(x + 4)$$

30. Graph the following function.

$$y = 5x + 2(x - 1) + 4(x - 6)$$

31. Graph the following function.

$$y = 6(x - 3) + 9x - 2(4x - 6)$$

32. The graphs in the figure below are incorrectly drawn. Identify the errors. Hint: Two errors exist in parts C and D.

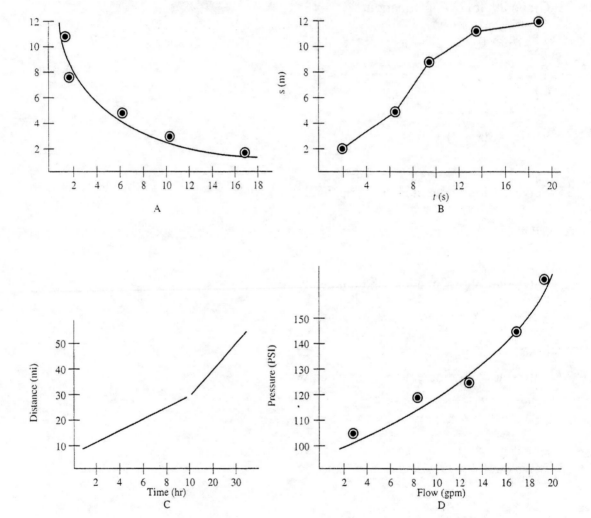

33. Use MATLAB to plot the sine wave with amplitude of 7 over the interval $0 \leq x \leq 2\pi$. Label x values on the x-axis. Label y values on the y-axis. Label the title of this graph, *The Sine Wave*.

34. Use MATLAB to plot the cosine wave with amplitude of 5 over the interval $0 \leq x \leq 2\pi$. Label x values on the x-axis. Label y values on the y-axis. Label the title of this graph, *The Cosine Wave*.

35. Use MATLAB to plot the tangent (tan) wave with amplitude of 2 over the interval $0 \le x \le 2\pi$. Label x values on the x-axis. Label y values on the y-axis. Label the title of this graph, *The Tangent Wave*.

36. Use MATLAB to plot the function $y = -2t + 3$ over the interval $-5 \le t \le 5$.

37. Use MATLAB to plot the function $y = \dfrac{1}{2}t + 6$ over the interval $-10 \le t \le 10$.

38. Use MATLAB to plot the function $y = 0.3t - 1$ over the interval $-20 \le t \le 20$.

39. Use MATLAB to change the color of the graph of Problem 36 for each case below:

   i)   black
   ii) green
   iii) red
   iv) yellow

40. Use MATLAB to change the color of the graph of Problem 37 for each case below:

   i)   magenta
   ii) yellow
   iii) cyan
   iv) white

   NOTE: For the interesting student on part iv), do some research in MATLAB literature of changing the background color from white to another color to visualize white graphs.

41. Use MATLAB to change the color of the graph of Problem 38 for each case below:

   i)   blue
   ii) black
   iii) green
   iv) red

42. Use MATLAB to generate the following cases for Problem 36:

a) black graph with the dash line style.
b) red graph with the dash-dot line style.
c) cyan graph with the dotted line style.
d) green graph with the solid line style.

43. Use MATLAB to generate the following cases for Problem 37:

a) magenta graph with the solid line style.
b) cyan graph with the dotted line style.
c) red graph with the dash-dot line style.
d) blue graph with the dash line style.

44. Use MATLAB to generate the following cases for Problem 38:

a) blue graph with the dash-dot line style.
b) yellow graph with the dash-dot line style.
c) black graph with the solid line style.
d) red graph with the dash line style.

45. Use MATLAB to generate the three graphs over the interval [-5, 5] in increments of 1.

$$\text{Graph 1} \quad y(x) = -2x + 3$$

$$\text{Graph 2} \quad z(x) = \frac{1}{3}x + 1$$

$$\text{Graph 3} \quad q(x) = -x + 4$$

Graph	Color	Line Style	Marker
Graph 1	red	solid	asterisk
Graph 2	black	dash-dot	cross
Graph 3	green	dotted	diamond

46. Use MATLAB to generate the two graphs over the interval $0 \le t \le 2\pi$ for 50 data points.

Graph 1 $y(t) = \cos(\pi t)$

Graph 2 $p(t) = 2 \sin\left(\dfrac{\pi}{6} t\right)$

Graph	Color	Line Style	Marker
Graph 1	blue	solid	circle
Graph 2	black	dash	cross

HOMEWORK FOR CHAPTER 10

Use the following data sets A – F as required.

Set A   Ages of people that attended an Alcoholics Anonymous (AA) therapy session: 25, 44, 20, 37, 56, 51, 34, 41, 36, 61, 33, 31, 47, 63, 67

SET B   Grades on the second test of ECT 120 class: 77, 80, 87, 67, 88, 77, 12, 93, 78, 44, 71, 86, 40, 100, 76, 83, 66, 62, 89, 79, 81, 52, 30, 71, 76, 100, 74, 65, 82, 100, 56, 35, 51, 59, 29,13, 71

SET C   Number of defective resistors per package of 100: 5, 10, 3, 2, 1, 9, 4, 10, 5, 3, 5, 5, 7, 11, 20

SET D   States within the USA with National Parks:

STATE	Number of National Parks
Alaska	8
Arizona	3
Arkansas	1
California	8
Colorado	2
Florida	3
Hawaii	2
Idaho	1
Kentucky	1
Maine	1
Michigan	1
Minnesota	1
Montana	2
Nevada	2
New Mexico	1
North Carolina	1
North Dakota	1
Oregon	1
South Dakota	2
Tennessee	1
Texas	2
Utah	5
Virginia	1
Washington	3
Wyoming	2

SET E Normal Monthly Precipitation in Miami Florida. Data taken over 30 years from 1961- 1990.

Month	Precipitation Inches (in.)
January	2.01
February	2.08
March	2.39
April	2.85
May	6.21
June	9.33
July	5.70
August	7.58
September	7.63
October	5.64
November	2.66
December	1.83

SET F Annually Year Precipitation in selected US Cities. Data taken over 30 years from 1961- 1990.

City	Precipitation Inches (in.)
New York City	47.25
Dodge City, KS	21.49
Detroit, MI	32.62
Honolulu, HI	22.02
Atlanta, GA	50.77
Hilo, HI	129.19
Tallahassee, FL	65.71
Orlando, FL	48.11
Bakersfield, CA	5.72
Alamosa, CO	7.57
Chicago, IL	35.85
Los Angeles, CA	14.77
Bridgeport, CT	41.66
New Orleans, LA	61.88
Las Vegas, NV	4.13
Binghamton, NY	36.99
Dallas, TX	33.70
Houston	46.07
Seattle	38

1. Construct a frequency distribution table for the indicated data set.

   a. SET A

   b. SET B

   c. SET C

   d. SET D

   e. SET E

   f. SET F

2. Use MATLAB to construct a histogram for the indicated data set.

   a. SET A

   b. SET B

   c. SET C

   d. SET D

   e. SET E

   f. SET F

3. Use Microsoft Excel to construct an absolute frequency polygon for the indicated data set.

   a. SET A

   b. SET B

   c. SET C

   d. SET D

   e. SET E

   f. SET F

4. Use Microsoft Excel to construct a relative frequency polygon for the indicated data set.

    a. SET A

    b. SET B

    c. SET C

    d. SET D

    e. SET E

    f. SET F

5. Determine the mean, median, and mode for the indicated data set.

    a. SET A

    b. SET B

    c. SET C

    d. SET D

    e. SET E

    f. SET F

6. Determine the range, standard deviation, and variance for the indicated data set.

    a. SET A

    b. SET B

    c. SET C

    d. SET D

    e. SET E

    f. SET F

7. Using the indicated data set, determine the range of values one standard deviation from the mean.

   a. SET A

   b. SET B

   c. SET C

   d. SET D

   e. SET E

   f. SET F

8. Use MATLAB to generate a straight-line (1st Order) approximation for the indicated data set.

   a. SET A

   b. SET B

   c. SET C

   d. SET D

   e. SET E

   f. SET F

9. Use MATLAB to generate a quadratic (2nd Order) approximation for the indicated data set.

   a. SET A

   b. SET B

   c. SET C

   d. SET D

   e. SET E

   f. SET F

10. Use MATLAB to create a graph that shows the 1st Order, 2nd order and 10th order curves on the same graph.

   a. SET A

   b. SET B

   c. SET C

   d. SET D

   e. SET E

   f. SET F

11. Jacklyn scored 100, 95, 80, and 92 on her last four calculus tests. What must she score on the last test in order to earn the grade of A? The grading scale of an A is 90 – 100.

12. Ms. Alicia Renee McCormick's Report Card

Course Credit	Course Letter Grade
4	B
3	C
3	A
1	A
3	B
3	A

4 – Point System A = 4.0, A- = 3.7, B+ = 3.3, B = 3.0, B- = 2.7, C+ = 2.3, C = 2.0, C- = 1.7, D+ = 1.3, D = 1.0 and F = 0.0

   What is Alicia's GPA based on the 4-Point system?

13. Below is Tom's grade distribution and recorded scores from his physics class. What is Tom's grade (weighted average)?

   Sample Grade Distribution Chart

HW	10% [Drop the lowest]
Midterm	30%
Final	30%
Quiz	20% [Drop the lowest]
Lab Reports	10%

HW:	25	60	90	85	100	100	100	100	95
Quiz:	65	75	100	69	100	100	100	100	100
Lab Reports:	80	90	85	80	85	90	85	100	100
Midterm:	85								
Final:	88								

14. What is Tom's grade using the following grading scale? Refer to question 13.

Grade	Point Range
A	95-100
A-	90-94
B+	87-89
B	84-86
B-	80-83
C+	77-79
C	74-76
C-	70-73
D+	67-69
D	60-67
F	0-59

15. The following table below shows the correlation between high murder rates and the number of McDonald's restaurants present in those cities. Use MATLAB to create a graph that shows the 1st Order, 2nd order and 10th order curve fitting of the number of McDonald's restaurant and total murders.

City	Total Population	Total Murders	Murders Per 100,000 People	Number of McDonald's Restaurants Present
New York, NY	7,319,546	1,220	14.2	312
Newark, NJ	260,232	175	9.0	10
Los Angeles	3,466,211	1,682	18.3	410
Sacramento, CA	375,845	114	7.9	30

APPENDIX B

CONVERSION FACTORS

Time

1 day = 1.44×10^3 min = 8.64×10^4 s
1 year = 8.76×10^3 h = 5.26×10^5 min = 31.5×10^7 s
1 h = 60 min = 3600 s
1 min = 60 s

Displacement (Length)

1 meter (m) = 100 cm = 1000 mm = 39.4 in = 3.28 ft
1 centimeter (cm) = 10 millimeters (mm) = 0.394 in
1 kilometer (km) = 10^3 m = 0.621 mi = 3280.8 ft
1 foot (ft) = 12 in = 0.305 m = 30.5 cm
1 inch (in) = 0.0833 ft = 2.54 cm = 0.0254 m = 25.4 mm
1 mile (mi) = 5280 ft = 1.61 km = 1760 yd
1 yd = 3 ft = 36 in = 0.9144 m
1 revolution = 360° = 2π rad

Area

1 m^2 = 10^4 cm^2 = 1.55×10^3 in^2 = 10.76 ft^2
1 cm^2 = $10^{-4} m^2$ = 0.155 in^2 = 100 mm^2
1 ft^2 = 144 in^2 = $9.29 \times 10^{-2} m^2$ = 929 cm^2
1 yd^2 = 9 ft^2
1 ft^2 = 144 in^2

Volume

1 m^3 = 10^3 liters (L) = 10^6 cm^3 = 35.3 ft^3 = 6.10×10^4 in^3
1 ft^3 = 1728 in^3 = 2.83×10^{-2} m^3 = 28.3 L

Velocity (Speed)

1 m/s = 3.28 ft/s = 2.24 mi/h = 3.60 km/h
1 ft/s = 0.305 m/s = 0.682 mi/h = 1.10 km/h
60 mi/h = 88 ft/s
1 km/h = 0.278 m/s = 0.913 ft/s = 0.621 mi/h
1 mi/h = 1.47 ft/s = 0.447 m/s = 1.61 km/h
1 rpm = 0.10472 rad/s
60 rpm = 1 cps = 1 Hz

Mass

1 kilo-gram (kg) = 10^3 grams (g) = 0.0685 slug
1 kg = 2.2 pounds (lb) = 2.2046 lbm
1 slug = 14.6 kg
1 slug = 32.2 lb
1 g = 1000 mg

Force

1 newton (N) = 0.225 lb = 3.60 ounces (oz)
1 pound (lb) = 16 oz = 4.45 N
1 lb = 0.454 kg = 454 g

Pressure

1 pascal (pa) = 1 N/m^2 = 2.09 × 10^{-2} lb/ft^2 = 1.45 × 10^{-4} lb/in^2
1 lb/in^2 = 144 lb/ft^2 = 6.90 × 10^3 N/m^2
1 atmosphere (atm) = 1.013 × 10^5 N/m^2 = 14.7 lb/in^2
1 kPa = 20.89 lb/ft^2

Work (Energy, Torque)

1 joule (J) = 0.738 ft-lb = 2.39 × 10^{-4} kcal = 0.0009485 Btu = 6.24 × 10^{18} eV
1 foot-pound (ft-lb) = 1.36 J = 1.29 × 10^{-3} Btu = 3.25 × 10^{-4} kcal
1 kilocalorie (kcal) = 4185 J = 3.97 Btu = 3077 ft-lb
1 Btu = 0.252 kcal = 778 ft-lb = 1054.8 J
1 kilowatthour (kWh) = 3.6 × 10^6 J = 3.6 MJ = 2.655 × 10^6 ft-lb

Power

1 watt (W) = 1 J/s = 0.738 $\dfrac{\text{ft - lb}}{\text{s}}$ = 0.001341 hp
1 kilowatt (kW) = 10^3 W = 1.34 hp

1 horsepower (hp) = 550 $\dfrac{\text{ft - lb}}{\text{s}}$ = 745.7 W = 33,000 $\dfrac{\text{ft - lb}}{\text{min}}$

Temperature

$$T_C = \frac{5}{9}\left(T_F - 32°\right)$$

$$T_F = \frac{9}{5}\left(T_C + 32°\right)$$

APPENDIX C

METRIC OR SI PRE-FIX CHART

Prefix	Symbol	Value
Tera-	T	10^{12}
Giga-	G	10^9
Mega-	M	10^6
Kilo-	k	10^3
Hecto-	h	10^2
Deka-	da	10^1
Base Unit	--------	$10^0 = 1$
Deci-	d	10^{-1}
Centi-	c	10^{-2}
Milli-	m	10^{-3}
Micro-	μ	10^{-6}
Nano-	n	10^{-9}
Pico-	p	10^{-12}

APPENDIX D

MATHEMATICAL REFERENCE TABLES
ENGLISH-METRIC EQUIVALENTS

LENGTH MEASURE

1 inch (in) = 25.4 millimeters (mm)
1 inch (in) = 2.54 centimeters (cm)
1 foot (ft) = 0.3048 meter (m)
1 foot (ft) = 12 inches (in)
1 yard (yd) = 3 feet (ft)
1 yard (yd) = 36 inches (in)
1 yard (yd) = 0.9144 meter (m)
1 mile (mi) = 1.609 kilometers (km)
1 millimeter (mm) = 0.03937 inch (in)
1 centimeters (cm) = 0.39370 inch (in)
1 meter (m) = 3.28084 feet (ft)
1 meter (m) = 1.093 61 yards (yd)
1 kilometer (km) = 0.62137 mile (mi)

1 rod = $16\frac{1}{2}$ feet (ft)

1 rod = $5\frac{1}{2}$ yards (yd)

1 statute mile = 5,280 yards (yd)

AREA MEASURE

1 square inch (in^2) = 645.16 square millimeters (mm^2)
1 square inch (in^2) = 6.4516 square centimeters (cm^2)
1 square foot (ft^2) = 0.092903 square meters (m^2)
1 square foot (ft^2) = 144 square inches (in^2)
1 square yard (yd^2) = 0.836127 square meters (m^2)
1 square yard (yd^2) = 9 square feet (ft^2)
1 square millimeter (mm^2) = 0.001550 square inches (in^2)
1 square millimeter (mm^2) = 0.000001 square meter (m^2)
1 square centimeter (cm^2) = 0.15500 square inches (in^2)
1 square centimeter (cm2) = 0.0001 square meters (m^2)
1 square decimeter (dm^2) = 0.01 square meter (m^2)
1 square dekameter (dam^2) = 100 square meters (m^2)
1 square hectometer (hm^2) = 10,000 square meters (m^2)
1 square meter (m^2) = 10.763910 square feet (ft^2)

1 square meter (m^2) = 1.19599 square yards (yd^2)
1 square kilometer (km^2) = 1,000,000 square meters (m^2)
1 square rod = 30.25 square feet (ft^2)
1 acre = 160 square rods
1 acre = 4,840 square yards (yd^2)
1 acre = 43,560 square feet (ft^2)
1 square mile = 640 acres

VOLUME MEASURE FOR SOLIDS

1 cubic inch (in^3) = 16.387064 (cm^3)
1 cubic foot (ft^3) = 0.028317 (m^3)
1 cubic foot (ft^3) = 1,728 cubic inches (in^3)
1 cubic yard (yd^3) = 0.764555 (m^3)
1 cubic yard (yd^3) = 27 cubic feet (ft^3)
1 cubic centimeter (cm^3) = 0.061024 cubic inches (in^3)
1 cubic centimeter (cm^3) = 0.000001 cubic meters (m^3)
1 cubic millimeter (mm^3) = 0.000000001 cubic meters (m^3)
1 cubic meter (m^3) = 35.314667 cubic feet (ft^3)
1 cubic meter (m^3) = 1.307951 cubic yards (yd^3)
1 cubic decimeter (dm^3) = 0.001 cubic meter (m^3)

VOLUME MEASURE FOR FLUIDS

1 gallon (gal) = 3,785.411 cubic centimeters (cm^3)
1 gallon (gal) = 3.785411 liters (L)
1 quart (qt) = 0.946353 liters (L)
1 ounce (oz) = 29.573530 cubic centimeters (cm^3)
1 cubic centimeter (cm^3) = 0.000264 gallon (gal)
1 liter (L) = 0.264172 gallon (gal)
1 liter (L) = 1.056688 quarts (qt)
1 cubic centimeter (cm^3) = 0.033814 ounces (oz)

MASS MEASURE

1 pound (lb) = 0.453592 kilogram (kg)
1 pound (lb) = 453.592 grams (g)
1 ounce (oz) = 28.349523 grams (g)
1 ounce (oz) = 0.028350 kilogram (kg)
1 kilogram (kg) = 2.204623 pounds (lb)
1 gram (g) = 0.002205 pound (lb)
1 kilogram (kg) = 35.273962 ounces (oz)
1 gram (g) = 0.035274 ounces (oz)

APPENDIX E

MEASUREMENTS

LENGTH

1 foot (ft) = 12 inches (in) = 0.3048 (m)
1 yard (yd) = 3 feet
1 yard = 36 inches = 0.9144 (m)
1 mile (mi) = 5280 feet (ft)
1 mile = 1760 yards (yd)
1 millimeter (mm) = 0.001 meter (m)
1 centimeter (cm) = 10 millimeters (mm)
1 centimeter (cm) = 0.01 meter (m)
1 decimeter (dm) = 0.1 meter (m)
1 decimeter (dm) = 10 centimeters (cm)
1 meter (m) = 100 centimeters (cm)
1 dekameter (dam) = 10 meters (m)
1 hectometer (hm) = 100 meters (m)
1 kilometer (km) = 1,000 meters (m)

LIQUID

1 cup (c) = 8 fluid ounces (oz)
1 pint (pt) = 2 cups
1 pint = 16 ounces (oz)
1 pint = 4 gills
1 quart (qt) = 2 pints
1 gallon (gal) = 4 quarts (qt)
1 imperial gallon = 1.2 US gallons (gal)
1 liter (L) = 1000 meters (m)
1 liter (L) = 1 cubic decimeter (dm^3)
1 milliliter (mL) = 0.001 liter (L)

WEIGHT

1 pound = 16 ounces (oz)
1 pound = 0.4536 kilogram (kg)
1 short ton = 2,000 pounds (lb)
1 long ton = 2,240 pounds (lb)
1 long ton = 1,016 kilograms (kg)
1 milligram (mg) = 0.001 gram (g)
1 centigram (cg) = 0.01 gram (g)
1 decigram (dg) = 0.1 gram (g)

1 gram (g) = 0.0352 ounce (oz)
1 kilogram (kg) = 1,000 grams (g)
1 kilogram = 2.2046 pounds (lb)
1 metric ton = 2,204.6 pounds (lb)
1 metric ton = 1,000 kilograms (kg)